To
The Art Club of
Philadelphia,
with the compliments
of the author.
Otis Skinner
1928

MAD FOLK OF THE THEATRE

George Anne Bellamy

MAD FOLK
of the
THEATRE

Ten Studies in Temperament

by

OTIS SKINNER

Author of
Footlights and Spotlights

ILLUSTRATED

THE BOBBS-MERRILL COMPANY
PUBLISHERS INDIANAPOLIS

Printed in the United States of America

To

C. O. S.

"O, ROSE OF MAY!"

FOREWORD

If in composing these sketches I have stepped unwarrantably into the office of the meticulous historian, I crave mercy of my readers. Whenever I have seen a date on the road ahead I have dodged into a hedge and hid until the abhorred thing had passed by, though sometimes it seizes me by the throat when I am not looking and refuses to let go until I cry Peccavi.

"Very well," you say, "if that is the best you have to offer why do you do this thing at all? The annals of the British stage are obtainable in every public library. Hundreds of volumes of 'lives,' criticism, intimate portraits, correspondence and gossip have given us complete account of the achievements of these children of Thespis. We know the parts they played, those in which they met with failure and those on which they left the mark of individuality and success. Great painters have limned their figures, their faces, in and out of character, and we know what they looked like. We have vivid sketches of their private lives, records of their ancestry and their sayings. It is a twice-told tale, why tell it again?"

Merely because in going over the old stories this small group seemed to step out from their pages and become animate. They were actors who reflected the age and body of their time, not chronological figures. Who were they? What were their habits, their thoughts, their ambitions, their emotions, their idiosyncrasies?

As an actor I saw myself in their company, intrigued by their vanities, loving their weaknesses and glorying in their successes. They became people I had known and acted with, particularly the incomparable Edmund Kean, whom I had loved from my boyhood. As they became articulate the urge seized me to commit to paper the words they spoke to me, the cinematic sequence of their doings and experiences. No need to distort the records for that, for it was in the very language of these accredited records they spoke. I need not novelize them or dramatize them, they themselves were novels and characters in plays.

What most impresses me in them is their modernity. Despite a background ranging from Charles II, through the "macaroni" period of the Georges to the Victorian era, they are not very different from the matinée idols of yesterday and the Hollywood heroes and heroines of to-day.

It is persistent, this atmosphere of romance. In our hard-boiled age of commercialism the actor, with his rank in the social set, his clubs, his California villa, his yacht and his press agent still finds it breath of life to his nostrils, as did the player folk of other years whose social status was scarcely better than that of shopmen or servants.

They are a somewhat sorry little group and for the most part a trifle mad. I feel, however, that they present the Thespian temperament as well, perhaps better, than others whose conduct was hedged about with stricter propriety. With their rebellious and scrambled emotions they yielded, unschooled, to the impulse of the moment, never heeding the lesson of inhibition.

This was, in a way, what made them good actors. Their feelings rushed over them in a "very torrent, tempest and whirlwind of passion"—and yet, in their acting, they learned to harness these surges, turning them into the service of art and begetting "a temperance that may give it smoothness."

Far be it from me to proclaim unrestrained, unconsidered emotionalism a foundation of art. Nothing is further from the purpose of playing than a spendthrift display of hysteria. The ideal actor is he who observes the hysteria of others and never allows it in himself. He is a spirit thermometer that registers the temperature and doesn't come out of his tube.

Nor do I hold a brief for looseness of morals. Standing a pillar of propriety among this coterie of wayward children is Thomas Betterton, a very Puritan of the theatre, in an age when puritanism had become almost abhorrent in men's minds, a man of frugality and exemplary conduct who took his art, his profession and his habits very seriously. His is the more notable example for its background of the lurid laxity of the Restoration. But nothing in his rigid standards prevented his becoming a colossal figure of the stage in his time.

FOREWORD

To George Anne Bellamy, who is the least important, I have given the most space. She had been so naïvely garrulous in her confidences to her Apology that I was loath to let the pretty soul do ought but prattle on that I might the better present her to those who had never heard of her. She did not mean so very much in the records of the stage, but hers was a career full of color and her experiences show the temper of her time.

To Nell Gwinn, the profane elf of Charles II's Court, I present my profound gratitude. No figure in the story of the stage offers greater opulence of gaiety, fascination, vulgarity and common sense. She was sunshine in dark ways—a fine purgative to the morally bilious Charles.

The three Madmen bring the line close to the memory of living men in America. They were noteworthy, not only for their own great achievements in acting, but for what they meant to the development of the American theatre.

My failure to dignify my list by the inclusion of the talented Garrick, the sprightly Sheridan, the ponderous Kemble and the majestic Siddons, perhaps the most worthy figures in English stage lore, is an arbitrary action that may be either condemned or forgiven. (It depends on how one looks on these things.) So much calculated observance of good form enshrouds them that I could not find it in my heart to allow their inclusion in the assembly of ne'er-do-weels presented in the following pages. Although brief glimpses of these aristocrats of the playhouse are to be found there, I feel that any further attention to them on my part would annoy them.

But if it will be of any consolation to them, I offer them my most humble apology.

O. S.

Capri
September, 1927

CONTENTS

LIST OF ILLUSTRATIONS

I

"HIS MAJESTIE'S SERVANT"

MAD FOLK OF THE THEATER

I

"HIS MAJESTIE'S SERVANT"

UNLESS it be the moment when, after an hour's fruitless whipping of a discouraging stream with every fly in your book from Brown Hackle to Scarlet Ibis, your rod tip bends and your taut line sings to the tug of a two-pound trout, I know no thrill that is comparable to that of the unexpected find of a rare volume in an obscure and shabby book shop. Even that comparison is feeble when the book is one you long have coveted; the thrill lasts longer and its recurrent waves radiate from the stone-splash of your discovery until they are stayed on the shores of your library shelves, and there they lap in much content.

You devoutly hope the moldy dealer, who never pays any attention to you or your prowling through his dusty rubbish, doesn't really know what he has got.

What you have found is in a miscellaneous lot containing GREEN'S ARITHMETIC, a novel by Marie Corelli, a copy of the LAWS OF INDIANA for 1869 and

McGuffey's Fifth Reader. How it ever had got into such abandoned company heaven knows!

Your predatory instincts are aroused. May a beneficent providence keep that mole of a bookseller's eyes blind to its worth!

Picking up the McGuffey you ask its price of the indifferent old party; he gives you one which you pretend to regard as shockingly high, and tell him so. You find an eighteenth-century volume of Sermons in a sacredly-shabby calf binding. You don't want it, of course—you never read sermons—but you get the dealer's valuation. It is so absurdly low that you are really tempted, but what would you do with the old thing anyway?

Then, still stalking your prey, your ear alert for the tinkle of the shop door-bell that announces another customer who may catch you at your little game, you lift up a tied bundle of Graham's Magazines from a dirty corner; they don't interest you either. You stroll to a neighboring rack and pick out a geography; you fancy your criminal procedure quite perfect—you are a fraud and you know you are, but you wonder if the dealer knows it, too; he has seen people like you before. Your face is a mask; you are doing the best acting of which you are capable as you saunter back to where your treasure lay—it is still there. After pawing over the entire batch of stuff you ask the price of *your* book. The cunning rascal! he knows its worth. You have wasted a lot of your valuable time. But no matter, its price is gratifyingly modest—you would have to pay three times the sum in any advertised book list.

What I found was in a back-street shop, down South, whose window displayed not only books but some oil lamps, glazed mantel figures, a tray of jumbled silver articles, another of old coins, and a Seth Thomas clock.

It has borne its years quite bravely. The credit on the title page is:

LONDON
Printed for Robert Gosling at the Mitre
Near the Inner Temple Court in Fleet Street,
1710. Price 3s.6d.

It is the Life of the eminent and respectable Mr. Thomas Betterton, who died shortly before the date of its publication and whose virtues are therein set forth with great naïveté. The work is anonymous, but pretty good authority ascribes it to one Gildon. Beyond doubt Gildon had much scorn for the theatre, for though the late eminent tragedian receives due laudation he seems to be a good deed in a naughty world. The material that made up the ranks of the acting profession in the days of the Merry Monarch and thereafter was, in this writer's opinion, a contemptible one.

It is sad that in our degenerate day we are even denied the privilege of looking back to the golden age of Mrs. Barry and Mrs. Bracegirdle—(what a fine, mouth-filling name—Anne Bracegirdle!)—as a period when the British stage was in flower. It would ease our conscience if we could look to a glorious background, though we are but poor inheritors of the tradition.

I learn, however, that even the revered Thomas had feet of clay; he imported a continental vice in introducing scenery for the first time in England for the mounting of one of his earliest plays, thereby bringing about his periwig a flood of censure. But how tolerant the biographer! He tells us that,

> "Others have laid it to the Charge of *Mr. Betterton* as the first Innovator on our rude Stage as a Crime; nay as the Destruction of good Playing; but I think with very little Shew of Reason, and little knowledge of the Stages of *Athens* and *Rome*, where, I am apt to believe was in their flourishing times as great Actors as ever played here before Curtains. For how that which helps the Representation, by assisting the pleasing Delusion of the Mind in regard of the Place, should spoil Acting, I cannot imagine, . . . since the Audience must be often puzzled to find the Place, and Situation of the Scene, which gives great Light to the Play, and helps to deceive us agreeably, while they saw before them some *Linsey-Woolsey* Curtains, or at best some piece of old Tapestry fill'd with awkerd Figures, that would almost fright the Audience."

This was in 1662. The long night of Puritan nightmare was over and the theatre was emerging from its ten-year sleep under the ban of the Commonwealth. The young King was endeavoring to make England forget Cromwell by dazzling it with court gaieties and providing amusement for a people who were hungry for it. Charles' hunger was even greater than theirs: there had been little laughter for the Prince and his shabby court in their long exile, begging a bare existence on the Continent, badgered and driven from pillar to post and often wanting the sheer necessities of life.

The drama had ample support in two companies, the Duke of York's and the King's. Letters Patent were granted giving them the practical monopoly of play production, the actors of the King's company at Drury Lane, of which Betterton was afterward a member, being known as "His Majestie's Servants."

Charles' interest in the two organizations was mainly on the feminine side, and he was royally impartial; from the Duke's House he chose for his mistress Moll Davis, "an impertinent slut," who lasted over four years, presented Charles with a daughter, and was then totally eclipsed by Nell Gwinn of Old Drury. Nell had been successively street arab, fish peddler, tavern mountebank, orange girl in the theatre and finally Drury's brightest, merriest comedienne. She and her merry sisters properly scandalized our good author; he bemoans the character of the players, men and women, who could readily lend respectability to the theatre did they not:

"by their own loose Lives, by an open Contempt of Religion, and making Blasphemy and Profaneness the marks of their Wit and good Breeding; by an undisguised Debauchery and Drunkenness, coming on the very Stage in Contempt of the Audience when they were scarce able to speak a Word; by having little regard for the Ties of Honor and Common Honesty to say nothing of the Irregularities of the Ladies, which rob them of their Deference and Respect, that their Accomplishments of Person would else command from their Beholders, especially when set off to such an Advantage as the Stage Supplies in the Improvement of the Mind and Person.''

So warm does he wax on his topic that he suggests if the Culprits were—

''discarded on the Discovery of their Follies of that Nature, I dare believe that they would sooner get Husbands, and the Theatre lose Abundance of that Scandal it now lies under. For even our Times, as corrupt as they are, have given us Examples of Virtue in our Stage Ladies. I shall not name them, because I would draw no Censure on those who are *not named.''*

Somehow, I think that unfair to the ''Examples of Virtue,'' but what could one expect from the Examples set by royal Charles and his cronies, Buckingham, Arlington and Rochester, companions of many a secret enterprise and all ''equally ready to empty a bottle, seduce a girl and write a sonnet or play!''

Though the censure of our anonymous recorder is in his own words it is undoubtedly that of the redoubtable Thomas Betterton himself who, perhaps, acquired his propensity for roasting by legitimate inheritance—he was the son of an undercook to Charles I. You hear the mellow thunder of his denunciation as, to his Boswell, he hands out this:

"When I was a young Player under *Sir William Davenant,* we were under a much better Discipline. We were obliged to make our Study our Business, which our young Men do not think it their duty to do; for they now scarce ever mind a Word of their Parts but only at *Rehearsals,* and come hither too often scarce recovered from last Night's Debauch; when the Mind is not very capable of considering so calmly and judiciously on what they have to study, as to enter thoroughly into the Nature of the Part, or to Consider the Variation of the Voice, Looks and Gestures, which should give them their true Beauty, many of them thinking the making a Noise renders them agreeable to the Audience, because a few of the Upper-Gallery clap the loud Efforts of their Lungs, in which their Understanding has no share. They think it superfluous Trouble to study real Excellence which might rob them of what they fancy more, Midnight, or indeed Whole Night's Debauches, and a lazy Remisness in their Business. Another Obstacle to the Improvement of our Young Players, is that when they have not been admitted above a Month or two into the Company, tho' their Education and former Business were never so foreign to Acting, they vainly imagine themselves Masters of that *Art,* which properly to attain, requires a studious Application of Man's whole Life. They take it therefore amiss to have the Author give them any Instruction; and tho' they know nothing of the Art of Poetry, will give their Censure, and neglect or mind a Part as they think the Author and his Part deserves. Tho' in this they are led by

Fancy as blind as Ignorance can make it: and so, wandering without any certain Rule of Judgment, generally favor the bad and slight the good.''

'Tis marvel what little change has been wrought in the character of our young players since the Restoration!

As an eternal reproach to these stage goslings the noble war horse holds up the example of his estimable co-worker, Mrs. Barry who, he declared, would always ''consult the most indifferent Poet,'' and thereby often make acting successes of ''such Plays, as to read, would turn a Man's Stomach.''

As Thomas grew older he became grouchier. The poor man had his troubles for we read that at seventy-five having long been tortured ''with the Stone and Gout, the latter at last, by repellatory Medicines, was driven into his Stomach, which prov'd so fatal as in a few days to put an End to his Life. He was bury'd with great Decency in *Westminster Abbey.*''

Comforting thought—he was buried with *decency!* He must, indeed, have hailed the death angel with joy in that he could shuffle off the garment of a corrupt world and crawl into the clean shelter of the tomb. One may to-day make a pilgrimage to this last resting-place in the Abbey where his virtues are tabled and enshrined in the flamboyance of the age of Queen Anne.

But let us turn back the clock a little to more troubled times when the state was in sore travail.

Although it is far from curfew hour the passers-by at Charing Cross grow fewer. What life the street shows is listless and depressed. Men stride to their homes as to places of ill repute, glancing over their shoulders with a frown at the Parliamentarian soldier clattering past on a rangy horse.

Bookseller Rhodes sees no profit in them. Few come to his shop these days to purchase Bibles, tracts and hymn books and there is small use to keep his windows unshuttered any longer to-night.

"Closing hour, Thomas!" he calls.

Apprentice Betterton obeys with alacrity. He and his under-prentice, Kynaston, make short work of it. Yet these lads show no inclination to leave. Something is toward within the shop. Rhodes opens the door to a little back parlor that is hung with shabby linsey-woolsey curtains. Save for a dais at the back surmounted by a huge chair and a corner table heaped with thin folios, the room is almost bare of furniture.

An assortment of swords, spears and armor is heaped at one side, and behind the door tinseled stage costumes dangle from their pegs.

Was not Master Rhodes wardrobe keeper to the King's Company of Comedians at Blackfriars before his master's head was laid on the block?

"Hart is late," says young Betterton.

"Trust him," replied Rhodes, "he'll never fail us."

A likely lad, this Betterton, scarcely a figure for the theatre, more nearly a farmer's or a blacksmith's son, low, stocky and unyielding, but with an eye not lacking in spirit, a mouth eloquent with latent power. At sight of the paraphernalia of the theatre strewn about the room Betterton pulls from his pocket a tattered copy of Shakespeare's ANTONY AND CLEOPATRA and strides up and down conning the lines of *Antony*.

Kynaston vaults into the big chair and with his hands clasping his drawn-up knees, shoves himself back and closes his eyes muttering *Cleopatra's* glowing verse. It is no longer in the clear contralto of the pre-Cromwellian days when he was the admired heroine of all the Shakespeare plays—his voice has changed. But if he has grown out of his former exquisite femininity he is still a marvelously handsome boy.

A guarded rat-tat-tat at the outer door. Hart is standing out there with his foot on the threshold gazing down the street. Rhodes admits him through the lower half of the divided door and makes it fast again.

Hart is big with news: General Monk is marching down from the north with his army, he is but a few miles from London, they say he is to turn out the Parliament and bring Prince Charles back from exile. We shall have the theatre back again, no more acting in cellar rooms like conspirators!

"Very like," says Rhodes quietly; "meanwhile suppose we see what we may do with this." He raps the cover of the play book.

Kings, parliaments, puritans, armies and wars are forgotten, England melts into Egypt. The

Serpent of old Nile is winding her beautiful coils and Betterton is dying with love for her as *Antony*. Hart's ear-filling barytone enriches the lines of *Enobarbus*, and Rhodes cues the trio from the speeches of the lesser characters, pausing now and then to direct a new reading and a different piece of stage business.

Another month: General Monk has smashed the Rump Parliament with a swing of his sword. Rhodes has his license to establish a theatre at the Cockpit in Drury Lane with Betterton, Hart and Young Kynaston enrolled as members of his company. In a short year Charles is received with welcoming shouts in London. The theatre holds up its head in the sunshine of royal favor and Thomas Betterton is its prophet.

The pursuit of play-acting at this period was conducted under distressing circumstances. The auditorium of the theatre presented a most disorderly scene; the fashionable but dissolute women of the town appearing masked in the open boxes and receiving unconcernedly the noisy attentions of the beaux during the progress of the play. The conduct of these riotous gallants and coarse women rendered the place well-nigh intolerable to decent patrons. Performers were frequently jeered at and their efforts at stilted emotionalism greeted with drunken yawps and howls of execration. Orange girls, selected for their alluring appearance, under the leadership of an older woman styled "Orange Moll," pushed their way through the spectators of the pit clacking the virtues of their expensive fruits to the brawling crew who devoured the sweet juice and used the rinds to pelt at the actors. Not infrequently an insolent beau, bemused and heated with liquor, would lurch upon the stage from box or pit, or the so-termed "fop's corner" (there being no intervening row of footlights, albeit he had to beware lest in his assault he rip his finery and his laces on a sort of *chevaux de frise* topping the protecting orchestra rail) and start a pitched battle with the hapless actors, leading other noblemen to the fray, using furniture and scene properties and even drawing swords in earnest, the unlucky manager looking on the while despairing and helpless at the results of his own pandering to the doubtful privileges of the gallants of the town.

His was an early example of gouging the public; not satisfied with his legitimate profits in the takings at the door, he augmented them by the sale of special favors. The custom of the Elizabethan theatre had provided certain favored ones with seats on the stage itself where they sat cluttering the entrances and exits, puffing the smoke from their long pipes into the very faces of the players. This feature, annoying alike to actors and audience, had been banished by royal order, but like the ticket-speculating theatre magnates of to-day, the manager was not to be denied his graft. For a liberal tip distinguished beaux were admitted not only behind the scenes and into the greenroom, but into the very tiring rooms of the actresses, witnessing their rob-

Thomas Betterton

ing and disrobing and carrying on such scandalous conversations as would frequently put to flight the young serving girls attendant upon these saucy queans.

The scandal grew until even Charles pretended to be shocked and by an edict drove the practise out of vogue, forbidding the dressing-room privileges to the gilded fops, tearing the masks from the faces of the women spectators, and restoring decency to the course of the performance.

It is high time to see what manner of man is this Thomas Betterton; to do so it is best we go to Drury Lane on one of his *Hamlet* nights.

The theatre is well filled long before the curtain hour, as the lesser public who honor their Shakespeare and the acting of Betterton are avid for the events of the evening. It is a less rowdy crowd than that which occupied the boxes and pit on the previous evening when Wycherley's salacious COUNTRY WIFE drew the bucks, the rakes and the wanton ladies of the town, nevertheless the auditorium is animated and noisy. The real play-lovers fill the balconies, for the most part they know nearly every line of the tragedy they love so well.

Down in the pit, partly benched and part standing room, is the usual mixed rabble of the well-to-do, officers in semi-uniform, East India merchants talking trade, brokers from the Exchange matching prices for to-morrow, three or four liberal-minded clergymen, critics, pamphleteers, London aldermen, rich shopkeepers, lawyers, members of the Parliament, poets, dramatists, a sprinkling of actors who are out of the bill, frequenters of the coffee houses, men about town. There is a fair representation of the fops as well, though this is not one of their nights; they form a group by themselves over in the corners where they may flirt with the beauties in the boxes.

The orange girls are busy, now and then getting into an altercation over rights in a certain customer, possibly that red-faced alderman who encourages both sides to a hair-pulling match. A ribboned gallant steals an orange from the basket of one of the venders, she retrieves it and bestows a volume of Billingsgate on the filcher. He retorts with some lewd proposals, and while his jeweled fingers steal down her plump neck receives a smart slap on the cheek. She moves on with her wares, quite happy and unruffled—it is all part of the game.

The boxes are animated with beauty, gay costumes, fashionable chatter, spirited repartee, lively disputes and screams of laughter; complacent Lords sit majestic, silent and stupid, masked ladies wave their fans to gallants in the opposite boxes. A handsome soldier leans over the chair of a blonde little thing in rose-colored satin, the long curls of his periwig sweeping her bare bosom; she glances at the dozing elderly husband at her side, and gives an assenting nod to his proposal. As he moves away his hand trails a caress across her shoulder.

The candle trimmers are adjusting the lights—the play is about to begin. As the curtain rises there is still the gabble of the spectators but it soon hushes as the *Ghost* stalks into the affrighted presence of *Marcellus, Bernado* and *Horatio* upon the platform at Elsinore. The scene terminates with an audience intent on the play—expectant, silent.

Now a fanfare of trumpets and enter their Majesties of Denmark clad in the costume of Charles II—stately and formal; the sitters and standees in the wings make way respectfully for the procession. The *King* leads on Mrs. Barry as the *Queen*—she is greeted with hearty though orderly applause—then follows Betterton, and the plaudits continue for some moments. But we have received a shock of surprise and disappointment; we forget that we have projected ourselves back two centuries and a half. Here is no spirited David Garrick or graceful Spranger Barry, but an ill-formed squat gentleman whose black Court costume, laces and curled periwig are not sufficient to conceal the clumsy figure beneath them. The head is so large as to be almost out of proportion, the neck is short and thick and the shoulders stooped; to these are added a corpulent body, thick legs and large feet. The face that looks out from its framework of curls is broad and somewhat pock-fretted; in it are set two small but expressive eyes, capable of portraying an unusual variety of emotion. His arms, which are short and fat, are kept at rest, except at occasional intervals, his left hand lodged in his breast between his coat and his waistcoat, his right conveying the appropriate gesture to his speech.

This latter gives us a second disappointment; as he begins "'Tis not my inky cloak, good mother," it rasps and rumbles like the wooden works of an ancient clock. The entire personality of the man seems an anachronism.

But presently, as he listens to the tale of the spectral visitor, we are aware of something arresting, the voice drops its discordance, and in its strained attitude of listening excitement we lose all sight of the cumbersome figure with its unseemly costume.

Our ears have grown accustomed to the grandiloquence of speech, the weighty pauses and the formal emphasis. We yield to the majesty of demeanor as we yield to the spell of the perfect proportions of Sir Christopher Wren's St. Paul's Cathedral.

Now we question nothing. The scene with the *Ghost* takes place, and I shall let Mr. Colley Cibber tell you about it:

> "He opened with a pause of mute amazement; then rising slowly to a solemn, trembling voice, he made the *Ghost* equally terrible to the Spectator as to himself; and in the descriptive part of the natural Emotions which the ghastly Vision gave him, the Boldness of his Expostulation was still governed by Decency, manly, but not braving, his voice never rising into that seeming outrage, or wild Defiance of what he naturally rever'd."

Even the fops in the audience are silent—the orange girls spellbound.

Mr. Samuel Pepys is at the play and he says of

his *Hamlet,* "It is the best acted part ever done by man."

He had evidently won the loyalty of Mr. Pepys, who spoke of him as a serious, sober gentleman given to studious pursuits and bearing his riches and his honors with humility. Only once did he bring upon himself the reprimand of the Diarist who was surprised that, in a performance of MUSTAPHA, Betterton and his fellow-player, Harris, "could not contain for laughing in the midst of a most serious part from the ridiculous mistake of one of the men upon the stage; which *I did not like.*"—Neither, I am sure, would you or I.

But not for worlds would I rob the dear old man of his moment of mirth even though it be in a tragedy. If ever an actor earned the privilege of laughter it was he. Notwithstanding the unusual honor and homage paid to him, the highest salary he ever received was the lavish sum of five pounds a week, but upon this he was enabled to establish a home wherein domestic happiness ruled supreme. His wife adored him; they had been lovers from their youthful days when she played *Juliet* to his *Romeo.*

My little volume of Betterton's life, with its wealth of punctuation marks, its *s's* that look like *f's* and its capitalized nouns, is mainly a treatise on the art of acting as he conceived it. Little is left to nature or impulse; all is stately and measured, as we may fancy the general conduct of the performers in the windy tragedies and mannered comedies of the period, Otway, Dryden, Wycherley and Vanbrugh. It was scarcely to be expected of a gentleman clad in voluminous velvet garments trimmed with yards of lace, mounted on high-heeled buskins and all but extinguished under the ringlets of his periwig, that he should be anything but pompous and grandiloquent. It was not real life that the stage represented, but a mock reality, conventionalized, transformed and clothed in rhetoric. Passion went by rule, gaiety to the beat of the metronome, emotion was measured by the yard-stick, and dignity governed the manners of the mimic world.

But no exemplar of this school could compete with Betterton. He subdued his hearers to rapt attention by a majestic and magnetic control. Says Cibber:

"I never heard a line of tragedy come from him wherein my judgment, my ear and my imagination were not fully satisfied, which since his time I cannot say of any one actor whatsoever."

After his retirement into privacy and into the distresses of his Stone and Gout, a benefit performance was given him at the new theatre in the Haymarket on the seventh of April, 1709, on which occasion his old comrade, Mrs. Barry, declaimed this eulogy written by the poet Nicholas Rowe:

"Had you with-held your Favours on this Night,
Old Shakespeare's Ghost had risen to do him Right,
With indignation had you seen him frown
Upon a worthless, witless, tasteless Town:

Griev'd and Repining you had heard him say,
Why are the *Muses'* Labours cast away?
Why did I only write what only he could Play?"

When he took his wife into his embrace that night it was with a foreboding that all was not well—but notwithstanding the agony his gouty foot was causing him he gave her a kiss and a cheery word and was helped to his coach. Arriving at the theatre he was carried to his dressing-room, where he thrust his foot into cold water to reduce its swelling before he could even bear as much as a slipper upon it.

Waiting the veteran's appearance was an audience representative of the best that London could boast and packed from pit to gallery. In its welcome, as he came limping upon the stage as *Melantius* in THE MAID'S TRAGEDY, Betterton forgot his ills, and under a barrage of bravos and cries of loving approval, he acted to the end of the play with a miraculous renewal of his youthful fire.

He was never again seen publicly and in forty-eight hours he had reached the undiscovered Country in whose confines death's surcease came not only to his bodily woes but to his financial worries as well. He had ventured in an overseas enterprise that proved disastrous, and his benefit fund was of great assistance to his widow, although it was not long before this faithful soul followed her husband.

So passed from view a stately, splendid figure.

For more than fifty years, from Charles II to

Queen Anne, his had been the finest example of excellence among the Servants of Their Majesties.

No better description of him could be given than is contained in three words of the theatre license granted by King William:

THOMAS BETTERTON, GENTLEMAN.

II

MISTRESS NELLY

II

MISTRESS NELLY

Ranking high in the British peerage is the title of St. Albans. The present holder is the eleventh in descent from the child that was presented to a King of England by its madcap mother as evidence of her love and fealty.

And Charles II, although too busily engaged in the affairs of his harem to check up the accurate pedigree of many noble families, whose escutcheons have since emblazoned the pages of Burke and DeBrett, had in this case not the smallest doubt in the world of his paternity. Charles was of a generous nature and willingly credulous in respect to his fatherhood of many little red-faced morsels of humanity brought to him as tokens of his virility.

When in a public address to the throne the petitioner referred to His Majesty as "the father of his people" the witty Duke of Buckingham added, *sotto voce*, "Yes, of a good many of them." And after all, why should the first gentleman of Britain doubt a lady's word? Was he a more profligate prince than several English sovereigns since his time who have worn the garments of domestic virtue? It is to be doubted. His liaisons were public knowledge from their very beginnings and, to many of his subjects, rather a source of satisfaction. Concealment of them was never attempted. They were as open as the day, and a complaisant nation obligingly footed the bills.

But there was no question as to royal sponsorship in this breed of St. Albans, albeit the rich British blood in its veins bubbled from a source in the noisome purlieus of Coal Yard Alley in Drury Lane. Its streams flowed through many channels, it even ran through cathedral aisles and produced a Bishop of Hereford.

"Come here, you little bastard!" quoth Mistress Nell Gwinn.

"Od's fish!" cries Charles. "Is that proper respect to my child?"

"How else then may I name him, Sire?"

"Suppose we say, 'The Earl of Burford.' "

" 'Tis what I might expect from your Majesty's generous heart."

Nelly made a curtsey to the ground, then threw her arms about the neck of her royal lover in a transport of joy. The beauty of the boy lent grace to his title; he crept into his sire's pride and affections and when later the thirteen-year-old earl was raised to the dukedom of St. Albans and betrothed to the daughter of the Earl of Oxford, Nelly, "the indiscreetest and wildest creature that was ever in a Court," felt she had not lived in vain.

'Twas in truth rare distinction for a lad whose fat and unspeakable slut of a grandmother got drunk and was drowned in her own fish-pond.

That little Miss Gwinn was not wholly engulfed

in the stews and brothels of Coal Yard Alley is a cause of rejoicing to posterity. Something in that elfin wench with carrotty hair, dancing eyes and the tiniest feet and hands in England told her a great destiny awaited her. Not that she was a lily in a mud-puddle, far from it. In her earliest teens men sought her and found her willing. The playwright Lacy, Hart the actor, and a nameless person known to us only as a "city merchant" all disputed for her compliance and all were successful. A standard of morals was difficult to find in the seventeenth century. But notwithstanding her kinship to the alley cat, there was something cleanly and decent in her little soul that could not be wholly smirched.

I doubt if any woman of her class ever shot across the pages of English history bearing the burden of so much affection as Nell Gwinn. Lanes and streets in England bear her name, houses in which she is said to have lived are pointed out with pride to the curious; sweet-shops, tea-rooms, coffee-houses, hat emporiums in England and America are named after her; novels and plays have been built around her, and reproductions of the Lely portrait are popular everywhere. When she died, the honest Doctor Tenison, afterward Archbishop of Canterbury, "preached a notable sermon in praise of Ellen Gwinn." She was capable of continence even though it were ephemeral; she was moved by kindness, by sympathy; gratitude and pity were as native to her as her heart-beats, and a saving grace of humor kept her immune from much that was dangerous.

Her blunt truthfulness is delightful. Her servants idolized her.

Once in the days of her affluence, when she reigned at Court, her ears were assaulted by a fearful din in front of her house. She flew out to find a burly navvy lying prone, her coachman kneeling on his chest, hammering his skull on the pavement.

"What's this?" she demanded.

"He said you were no better than a common whore."

"Get up, you block-head! Never fight a man for telling the truth."

She was honest, she was loyal. Hypocrisy and she were mortal enemies and charity dwelt at her hearthstone. She never could have inherited these qualities from her grasping, blowsy mother; perhaps they were the gift of her father, a nebulous individual whose identity no one seems able to reveal to us. Probably he was legally and legitimately her sire, but who he was is in complete darkness; he is in much dispute—like Homer. Etherege, the lampoonist, in a coarse piece of doggerel wrote:

> "No man alive could ever call her daughter
> For a battalion of Armed men begot her."

As to Mother, there is no dispute about her, she was too scandalously known to escape identification and too much an intolerable nuisance to afford any kind of satisfaction to her daughter who, in the prosperity of her position at Court, was able to segregate her in a mansion house where she could comfortably drink herself into oblivion. But Nell was fond of the old harridan, and gave her a grand funeral with pomp, circumstance and 'scutcheons at St. Martin's Church, erecting a memorial tomb in which her own body was bestowed in after years.

Nelly's affairs of the heart covered a wide range, they began with a gamin and ended with a King. Her delightful account of the first of these has been preserved:

"My first love, you must know, was a link boy. God knows what has become of him. When I last saw him, he said he would love me humbly to my dying day. Poor Dick had the heart of a gentleman. He used to say I must have been a lord's daughter for my beauty; that I ought to ride in my coach, and behaved to me as if I did. When we had sold our oranges he would light me and my mother home to our lodgings in Lawkenor's Lane as if we had been ladies of the land. He said he never felt easy for the evening 'till he had asked me how I did, and if he saw us housed at night he slept like a prince. I shall never forget when he came flushing and stammering, and drew out of his pocket a pair of worsted stockings which he had bought for my naked feet. It was bitter cold weather, and I had chilblains which made me hobble about till I cried, and what does poor Richard do but work hard like a horse and buy me worsted stockings. My mother bade him put them on me; and so he did, and his warm tears fell on my chilblains, and he said he should be the happiest lord on earth, if the stockings did me any good."

Life never stood still with Nell. Restless as a

caged fox she moved from one occupation to another, obeying the urge for adventure. A slavey, and probably a practising neophyte in the squalid trade of the brothel where she was brought up, she escaped to the streets to peddle fish. A pretty sight it was, this tattered elf crying: "Herrings! Fresh Herrings!" under the noses of staid London citizens, who forgot their gravity to exchange slang with her and leave a few coppers in her dirty hand.

Then a shift to the fruit trade and another street cry: "Oranges! Chaney Oranges!" brought housewives to their windows to catch a glimpse of a tousled head, a roguish smile and a basket of golden fruit, whose virtues were piped in a shrill childish voice.

Little profit in it in these respectable streets—wasted breath! There's better trade in the taverns, where she can set down her burden and dance and sing naughty songs to the yells of delighted loafers. They try to take liberties with her and get her drunk. She is too wise an urchin for that—money never comes that way. She eludes their clumsy advances, her pocket sagging with the weight of copper coin and a few sixpences tied in the corner of her handkerchief.

But all roads are roads to Rome and to the stage door of Drury Lane.

With a novitiate in "Orange Moll's" delectable academy, a decent gown, a mob-capped head, yellow stockings and stout, buckled shoes, she joins the corps of orange girls with the grime dug out of her ears and the cleanest, prettiest hands in the Kingdom. Her success was instantaneous, her sister venders viewed this siren of fourteen with the rankest envy. The bewigged and beribboned gallants of the pit encircled her basket, enchanted with her cherry lips and her pert airs. These were dazzling moments for her, but far more wonderful were the long intervals when her wide eyes were fixed on the acted scenes. She was swept away, lost in the mazes of the never-never land where the brave figures and handsome faces of Mohun, Lacy and Hart shone like demigods.

It was with a far different gaze that she turned her eyes on the women. Those frumps who danced like stuffed marionettes and sang like magpies! No illusion there. Could she get up on that stage she could outdo the whole crew. With her agile feet and the witchery of her singing it was time she gave up vending oranges and showed them a few tricks. A hint of this to Orange Moll sent her sprawling with a box on the ear, her yellow fruit spewing in every direction.

"Now pick yourself up, you ugly young baggage! Dare to ape your betters and I'll give you what's what! You'll go packing!"

Nell hurled a rotten orange at the face of her tyrant and retreated wriggling her fingers at her nose. Three minutes later she was doubling with laughter over the antics of Cartwright and Wintershall in the scenes of *Falstaff* and *Slender* in THE MERRY WIVES OF WINDSOR.

A personality such as hers could not long be smothered in that pack of hussies in Drury Lane pit. She knew the art of wheedling, there were friends of high influence in the theatre. Whether it was Hart or Lacy, her theatre lovers, or the city merchant (Durgan, Duncan, Dorgan—whichever his name may have been) who saw an economical exit from his affair with Nelly, somebody gave her open sesame to the enchanted regions behind the footlights. It may have been the stately Thomas Betterton, at that time the presiding genius at the rival theatre, the Duke's House.

A biography published sixty-five years after Nell's death contains the astonishing statement that she sent for Thomas to visit her at her lodgings that she might urge the fulfillment of her wishes, but that "unlucky for Miss Gwinn Mr. Betterton was not amorous, or at least conceived no passion for her, for she was in hopes of operating upon the manager by her face and figure, as well as her voice and action."

What's this? The impeccable Thomas so far forgetting his dignity as to visit the bordellos of Lawkenor's Lane at the behest of a vagrom orange wench! Oh, fie!

It matters little who her sponsor was—the door was flung open, she pranced in on nimble toes and established her position at her own sweet will—a young wildcat in the tinseled coterie of players.

With her head stuffed with dreams of conquest in the realm of sentiment—of suffering heroines, betrayed ladies, wronged daughters, love-lorn maidens—she chose the romantic parts and succeeded in getting them. No doubt she was pretty bad; Samuel Pepys says she was. Of a production of Dryden's Indian Emperor he wrote that it was "a good play but not so good as people cry it up. I found Nell came again which I am glad of, but was most infinitely displeased with her being put to act the Emperor's daughter, which is a great and serious part which she does most basely"—adding that "Nell's ill speaking of a great part *made me mad.*" And Pepys was an impartial critic. He was inordinately fond of the saucy creature. When first presented to her by his mistress, Knep, behind the scenes of the King's Theatre he kissed her, so did his wife, and found her a "mighty pretty soul." The kiss left the sweetest of savors on his lips, and in his diary record for the day the climax of his pleasure is, "specially the kissing of Nell." In very truth he could not shake off the memory of that delicious moment. He yearned to surfeit his gaze on more charms than her face and lips afforded. His opportunity came. Meeting with Knep at the playhouse, "she took us up to the tireing rooms and to the women's shift where Nell was dressing herself and was all unready, and is very pretty, prettier than I thought." The sight so unnerved him that he found it necessary to walk for some moments, "all up and down the house—above and then below into the scene room"—before his senses ceased to spin. For several days after that visit Mistress

Knep found the Diarist completely distrait. He was avid enough in his calls at the playhouse, although he did not always find Mistress Gwinn in a frolicsome mood. Business was often bad at Drury Lane, to the disgust of the sprightly Nelly.

And though Pepys on one occasion feasted his eyes upon her when she came from the stage "in her boy's clothes, mighty pretty," he found the little vixen swearing like a trooper at the meager audience—"to see how Nelly cursed for having so few people in the pit was very pretty." I've no doubt that Nelly's cursing was in blunt Anglo-Saxon dirt, and that Mr. Pepys shrieked with delight over it.

Indecency with the salacious Samuel was like charity—it began at home. It was, moreover, a matter of time and the occasion. There were times when he could not abide it. Of Dryden's, AN EVENING'S LOVE, he wrote: "I saw this new play with my wife yesterday and do not like it, it being very smutty."

Delusion as to her dramatic *métier* tarried briefly with her; very soon she learned that Nell Gwinn and sadness were an ill-matched team. The comedy parts were turned over to her. Playwrights created gay characters, composed brilliant dialogue that from the lips of Drury's newest comedienne fell on delighted ears. From the tips of her toes and her fingers to the sparkle of her eyes she danced and the hearts of her audience danced with her. Furthermore, she danced into the wide-open arms of Lord Buckhurst.

That, however, was after the grim year when London's population died hourly like flies under the visitation of the Great Plague, when the theatres and every sort of shows and diversions were buried under a pall of silence, and, as Defoe said, "sadness and horror sate upon the countenances of the people; death was before their eyes and everybody began to think of their graves, not of mirth and diversions." Nights were made doubly hideous by the gatherers of corpses who drove their carts through streets lined with stricken homes, with the appalling cry, "Bring out your dead!"

What Nell was doing during this reign of terror is not known—her occupation in the theatre was gone. Probably living with Charles Hart or some one else who was good to her. But the Great Fire of London cleansed the town and put an end to the pestilence; Nell was back at the King's House, bringing smiles into the countenances of the saddened citizens once more.

To Buckhurst's smile she responded with a look of voluptuous gratification. Here, indeed, was a step upward! Charles, Lord Buckhurst, later Earl of Dorset and the first Earl of Middlesex, whom Walpole called "the finest gentleman in the Court of Charles II," was gay, handsome, witty—poet, satirist, sensualist and man of the world. His breeding and manners were of the best, and he had proved his courage in the Dutch wars.

Nelly's head whirled a little with the unexpected joy of her conquest. At that time she lodged at the

"Cock and Pye" in Drury Lane where, on a memorable May-day morning in 1667 when London woke to its first real rejoicing since the devastation of the plague came to its end, Pepys saw her.

The town was *en fête,* pipings, dancing and laughter took possession of the hearts of the people. May-poles were erected in the open spaces. Pepys was abroad drinking in the gaiety—and to cap it all was the charming vision in Drury Lane. "Thence to Westminster; in the way meeting with many milk-maids with their garlands on their pails, dancing with the fiddler before them; and saw pretty Nelly standing at her lodgings door in Drury Lane in her smock sleeves and bodice, looking upon one: she seemed a mighty pretty creature."

Buckhurst's passion took possession of him. If they were to be truly happy, she must away to a nest of delight far from town; he declined to share her with the playhouse. In Epsom, not then the scene of Derby racing but the resort of rich Londoners for its healing waters, they set up a merry house much to the distress of Pepys, who mourned her absence from the stage.

The liaison was fiery, racketty, intensive and brief. While it lasted they kissed and quarreled and laughed, and perhaps Nell wept a little. A well-matched pair they were, Buckhurst with his keen mind and Nelly with her unflagging spirits and bright wit. But

"These violent delights have violent ends
And in their triumph die."

Pepys supplies us with a bit of tattle picked up at the theatre concerning this episode. He hears that "Nell is already left by my Lord Buckhurst and that he makes sport of her, and swears she hath all she could get from him; and Hart, her great admirer, now hates her; and that she is very poor, and hath lost my Lady Castlemaine, who was her great friend, also; but she is come to the House, but is neglected by them all."

I doubt if this neglect dashed her spirits in any degree, she was always ready to meet the shifts of fortune for good or for ill. If poverty ever pursued her it never caught up with her.

Before many months Nell was bowing to a roar of satisfaction from a crowded house that welcomed her back to the theatre, and the enchanted Pepys was among them.

Here she wasted little time over the serious characters. If Samuel Pepys found fault with her for playing them she found as little satisfaction. In a prologue to the DUKE OF LERMA that was allotted to her, the poet made her say:

"I know you in your hearts
Hate serious plays—as I hate serious parts."

Complete emancipation from all sobriety was afforded her in an extravagant play called ALL MISTAKEN, OR THE MAD COUPLE. In this, both she and Hart captured the town in the rather coarse and indecent scenes of the mad lovers. Particularly was Pepys gratified by Nell in this piece which he damns as an ordinary play, "but only Nell's and Hart's mad parts are most excellent done, but especially hers, which makes it miracle to me how ill she do any serious parts, as the other day, just like a fool or a changling: and in a mad part do beyond imitation almost."

It was in this play that Nell had a huge success in her song that burlesqued a woeful ballad sung by Moll Davis at the rival theatre.

Little Miss Davis, an excellent dancer and singer, was an indifferent actress and a conscienceless minx who became mistress of the King and mother of a daughter whom he acknowledged to be his. The song that gave her celebrity and won the heart of the Merry Monarch was sung after she had performed a jig in a surpassing manner. Its opening verse ran:

> "My lodging is on the cold ground
>   And very hard is my fare,
> But that which troubles me most is
>   The unkindness of my dear.
> Yet still I cry, O turn, love,
>   And I prythee, love, turn to me,
> For thou art the man that I long for,
>   And, alack, what remedy?"

This song, says the old prompter, Downs, she gave so touchingly that "not long after it raised her from a bed on the cold ground to a bed royal."

The travesty in ALL MISTAKEN was sung by Nell, as the madcap heroine, to her fat lover.

Mirida:

"Lie still, my babe, lie still and sleep,
  It grieves me sore to see thee weep,
Were't thou but leaner I were glad;
  Thy fatness makes thy dear love sad.

My lodging is on the cold boards,
  And wonderful hard is my fare,
But that which troubles me most is
  The fatness of my dear.
Yet still I cry, O melt, love,
  And I pr'y thee now melt apace,
For thou art the man I should long for
  If 'twere not for thy grease."

In spite of the complete approval accorded her only in the comic characters it is curious to find her repeatedly appearing in sentimental rôles. This may have been the result of Charles Hart's jealousy and resentment; he held the theatre direction largely in his hands and he never forgave Nelly for throwing him over in the Buckhurst affair.

What time Nell was added to the King's galaxy of beauty is in some obscurity. According to an entry in Pepys's Diary in 1668, he had it from Mrs. Knep, that "the King did send several times for Nelly, and she was with him." She was then seventeen, wise beyond her years with a vocabulary acquired in Lawkenor's Lane, but riotous living had not harrowed too deeply the dainty, delectable morsel that she was.

Be that as it may, there is small question of her capture of Charles' affections when, as *Almahide* in

Dryden's CONQUEST OF GRENADA, she recited the prologue dressed in a ridiculous costume, crowned with a hat "made in the circumferance of a timber coach wheel."

The appearance of the diminutive creature under that umbrella of a hat was so droll that Charles could scarcely more than gasp, Odso! and Od's fish! and nearly suffocate with laughter. We are quite sure that he carried Nelly home in his coach that night. That it was not her first visit we are also sure, for about this time—in 1670—the Duke of St. Albans was born, the father King Charles, the mother Nell Gwinn, graduate of the slums, aged nineteen. She had achieved a place in the accredited harem which she never lost until, with his dying breath her regal lover implored his brother, James, not to "let poor Nelly starve."

But first there were preliminaries to arrange. What of this Charles, Lord Buckhurst? He is not going to give her up without recompense.

"Od's fish!" quoth the King. "Give him a diplomatic billet in France, and create him Earl of Middlesex."

Such gifts made no inroads on the privy purse—and they soothed wounded pride.

With the same ease that Nelly had, from her tenderest years, slipped into every position in which she had found herself she entered upon the life of the Court. So woefully taught had she been that she could scarcely write her own name, her general signature being a meandering E. G., scrawled at the end of letters written by her friends. She was not to the manner born, and she made no attempt to assume it. She brought her own manners with her, and they were shocking. But they pleased Charles immeasurably.

With the bluntest impudence she told him that he might be Charles the Second of England, but he was Charles the Third for Nelly—there were two of his predecessors of that name in the history of her ménage, Hart and Buckhurst.

For all his title's significance—"the Merry Monarch"—Charles was a somewhat wearied sovereign. Formality surrounded even his amours. He was not without his sense of humor—indeed it was quite keen. Witness his reply to the impudent jingle of Rochester:

> "Here lies our sovereign lord the King
> Whose word no man relies on;
> Who never said a foolish thing,
> And never did a wise one."

"The damned rogue is right," said Charles. "My *discourse* is my own, my *actions* my ministers'. As to my word let them take that up with my Parliament."

His was the rôle of the Grand Caliph who was lazily and luxuriously entertained by his various Sheherezadas. Often he was stung out of his inertia, as when Lady Castlemaine's shrewish tongue roused him to a show of opposition to her tantrums. Or when La Belle Stuart with her blonde seduction and tantalizing childish graces led him on to unwonted exertions of assault upon the citadel that would only yield at a price—perhaps even that of a share of the throne. In his frenzy he was almost ready to divorce his Queen and pay the forfeiture. But, for the most part, Charles was frankly bored.

Into the dull round of his pleasures Nell swept like a cyclone. Never had the King been so stimulated. Others of his mistresses were flagrant in their infidelities—Nell was faithful. Others of his favorites worked mightily for advancement, position, titles—Nell was content to be handsomely housed and provided for, to be the King's entertainer and to love him unselfishly. Her boy was a king's son, she had few fears for his future position—for herself she asked little.

She was not above playing scurvy jokes even upon the King. It is related that she found occasion to lure him incognito with a few courtiers into a house of ill repute where entertainment was provided and His Majesty induced to undress and go to bed. Having thus bestowed him she ran off with his clothes. The keeper of the place supplied him with garments then demanded payment for them and for all that had been provided. His Majesty hadn't a penny. He offered a costly ring from his finger as security. "Glass!" cried the man, "I know your kind. You can't diddle me out of my pay. I'm going to give you into custody." He was about to carry out his threat when some one recognized the King.

Courtesy of the Harvard College Library, Theatre Collection

Nell Gwinn in the Epilogue to *Sir Patient Fancy*

It is unlikely that when Charles took this wild, profane young hoyden under his protection he had any thought of the connection being one of permanence. To the dissolute, disillusioned Prince, who at thirty returned from an exile filled with treachery, rebuffs and hardships to mount the throne of his father, women were playthings, never intimates or disinterested friends. He had no illusions about the magnet of royal favor that drew them, nor was he blind to the motives of the Court intriguers who sought to fasten mistresses upon him to be used for their own political ends. For him sincerity, fidelity or chastity did not exist. He was amused and rather amazed to find that of all who ministered to his pleasures he could least spare Nell Gwinn. She brought a solace he did not find elsewhere. She understood his moods and never intruded upon them; she never reproached him for his flares of passion for other women, she knew that he would come back to her when he cooled. Moreover, she made him laugh and spoke his language, he could ill afford to lose consolation like that. She sang for him, she danced for him, gave imitations of his ministers and his mistresses that caused him to roar with delight.

After boresome conversations with Queen Catherine, tedious sessions with officials, fierce contentions with the Parliament and simpering sallies with Court beauties Charles can exchange the argot of the taverns and the streets with Nelly and take vast breaths of relief. He gives her a house in Pall Mall where he can visit her and throw aside etiquette and the affairs of State. Sometimes, particularly troubled, he brings his worries with him to be discussed with this young creature, roughly and wisely schooled in the ways of men and women.

The day has been one of nerve-racking petitions.

"How the devil, Nelly, am I to satisfy these people of England? They are tearing me to pieces with their clamors."

"Your Majesty could readily stop their tongues were you not so great a fool."

"Od's fish! What's this, you minx?"

"Dismiss your ladies and mind your business. Let the people of England go hang! They'll soon be satisfied."

"Come here and kiss me!" cries Charles.

John Evelyn, the chronicler, who never dipped his pen in scandal but to condemn it, had an opportunity of walking with the King—"through St. James' park to the garden where I both saw and heard a very familiar discourse between him and Mrs. Nelly, as they call an impudent comedian, she looking out of her garden on a terrace at the top of the wall and he standing on the green walk under it. I was heartily sorry at this scene. Thence the King walked to the Duchess of Cleveland, another lady of pleasure, and curse of our nation."

Although in the eyes of the austere Evelyn Nell is an "impudent comedian," and he writes that he seldom goes to the theatres where he finds "fowle and indecent women now, and never 'till now, permitted to appear and act, who, inflaming several young noblemen and gallants, became their misses and to some their wives," he at least never calls the slum-bred Nelly "the curse of the nation." That title he reserves for the highly-born Barbara Villiers, later Mrs. Palmer, who on securing the King's favor became the Countess of Castlemaine, and who so bedeviled the King that he created her Duchess of Cleveland to silence her clacking tongue.

Charles did not mind the Duchess' infidelities so much as he did her temper and her importunities. He was even unperturbed when he discovered the great Duke of Marlborough, then plain John Churchill, *flagrante delictu* with the Duchess. According to the story Churchill jumped out of the bedroom window. Charles merely looked after him, saying, "I forgive you, sir, for I know you do it for your bread!"

It is said the insatiable Barbara kept the handsome Churchill on her pay-roll. At all events, in July of 1672 the Duchess was delivered of a daughter and Charles said she was none of his.

Far different was the conduct of the vulgar but faithful Nell. She was for the King, none other. Once her passion for gambling had led her into a run of villainous luck and she found herself heavily in debt to Sir John Germaine.

"Easily paid, Nelly!" exclaimed the Knight. "Come to me and we'll tear up the account in the morning."

Nelly spat at him and bade him go back to his kennel.

"I am not such a poor sports-woman as to lay the dog where the deer should lie!"

For the death of his sister, the Duchess of Orleans, in France, the King showed a commendable amount of genuine grief. There was a rumor abroad that she had been poisoned; Charles was extremely perturbed about it. She had only a short time previously paid her brother a visit in London, bringing in her train a ravishing beauty, Louise de Querouaille. When the King's sorrow had sufficiently abated, he sent the Duke of Buckingham to Paris to negotiate the transfer of the lovely Louise to the English Court. Buckingham departed with joy. Anything to lessen the influence of his avowed enemy, the Duchess of Cleveland! Could this charming French girl be induced to accept the King's offer the outcome would give him an upper hand over the spiteful Barbara. He covertly suggested to Louis XIV that if Louise became mistress to Charles II she would still be faithful to the interests of France. Louis saw the advantage. When Mademoiselle arrived she was given magnificent apartments in Whitehall Palace. After seasonably holding off the King's advances she gracefully yielded and in due time the coronet of a duchess adorned the head of the newest favorite.

Charles was enraptured, the French diplomats were satisfied.

The long-suffering Queen Catherine sighed, shrugged her shoulders and sought comfort in her chapel. She was growing callous. Apart from the

Queen's retinue and the disgruntled Cleveland supporters all Whitehall paid court to the new beauty.

Nelly, however, sang no hymn of praise. She looked at the girl with a baby face and laughed—and the future Duchess of Portsmouth quite righteously hated her.

Thence onward it was a battle royal between the two with the odds heavily on Nelly's side. Not that she could in the least influence the King's passion for the dainty French girl, his infatuation was too overwhelming to be swayed by any tactics Nell might use—she was far too sensible to attempt the impossible. Charles to her was just a bad child who must have his own way or he would pull the house down over their ears.

It was in their personal skirmishes that the British beauty won over the French, an easy conquest and rather unfair. Louise had but little English, Nell never attempted to speak to her in her own tongue, but in any language whatever Nelly's wit would have borne down everything before it. She always addressed this new court flower as "Mrs. Carwell"—that being the nearest phoneticism she cared to make of Querouaille,—which pronunciation became the accepted one everywhere. She was having a thoroughly good time with the French doll, skilled though Mademoiselle was in every art of allure that an education in the Court of Louis XIV could attune to the sense of the King.

Louise's family was of ancient lineage, she never failed to make a show of sorrow over the deaths of royal personages intimating her own relationship to them. This was a source of never-failing amusement to Nelly. The King of Sweden died, Louise went into mourning. Directly after, the death of the King of Portugal was announced, Nelly went to the expense of procuring an elaborate costume of solemn black and wailed loudly to the amusement of the Court. Publicly embracing her rival she pretended to weep in her arms.

"Oh, sister!" she exclaimed, "let us agree to divide the world; you shall have the Kings of the North and I the Kings of the South."

This favorite form of joke Nell repeated when the Duchess went into mourning for the Prince de Rohan.

Dripping in sables Nelly came to Court, desolated beyond words, and ranged herself alongside the grief-stricken Louise.

She was asked the cause of her woe.

"Oh, haven't you heard of my loss? The Great Cham of Tartary is dead."

"And what the devil was the Cham of Tartary to you?"

"Just what the Prince de Rohan was to Mrs. Carwell."

The Court was never dull when Mistress Nelly was devising new pranks to play upon the Duchess. The common people of London became interested in the game, delighting in the discomfiture of Louise who was never a favorite among them. She was a foreigner, a Papist, a suspected tool of

Louis—XIV—these put her down in the black books of the populace. When an expensive service of plate was being completed as a present to Her Grace of Portsmouth the people crowded to the goldsmith's shop out of curiosity and "threw out their ill wishes against the Duchess; and wished the silver was melted and poured down her throat; but 'twas ten thousand pities his Majesty had not bestowed this bounty on Madam Ellen."

A coach was being driven through the streets of Oxford emblazoned with the royal coat-of-arms. Catching sight, through the window, of a pretty woman in Court costume a mob raced after the vehicle hurling obscene epithets against the occupant whom they took to be the Duchess of Portsmouth.

However it was Nelly who thrust out her bright face, imploring silence.

"Pray, good people, be civil!" she cried, "I am the *Protestant* whore."

In July, 1672, Louise gave birth to a son, who was so welcome that he was obliged to shoulder the titles of Baron of Settrington, Earl of March and Duke of Richmond, a terrible burden for a baby of three years to bear!

But it remains to be known that pretty Nelly gave Charles a Christmas present of a boy on the previous Day of Noël. As Louise had become a member of the King's household in September, 1670, it would seem that Nell Gwinn, too, had not been idle. This child was called James after the King's brother, made Lord Beauclerk and died in Paris when he was nine.

There came a time when Nell was made a Lady of the Privy Chamber in the Queen's household. This appointment by the King was not given in the spirit of satire or spitefulness; he did not love his Queen but he was not unkind to her according to his lights. Nell could not be otherwise than tender and considerate to the poor lonely lady whose crown of sorrow was that she was not able to present a child to her sovereign lord. I hope she made the Queen laugh. Out of her own abundant spirits she would gladly spare a little merriment for the melancholy Catherine of Braganza.

Days of dull and formal festivities came and went at Whitehall and at Windsor. His Majesty pursued his pleasures, played with his spaniels and watched their mating and their accouchements in the royal apartments, listened with amusement to malicious gossip which one faction leveled at the other, striving for the King's favor, lent his presence to plays and pageants, tried his hand at writing verse, made indolent love to new mistresses—and was eternally bored. Money was needed (for pleasure is costly) and he grew impatient when parliamentary machinery did not supply it at once. Petitions must be listened to. Life was filled with wearisome details.

Now and then a pretty face or two was purveyed to Whitehall by designing diplomats to spur his jaded senses, that of Hortense Mancini, niece of Cardinal Mazarin, outshining all the rest. At sight of this gorgeous creature Charles roused himself. What if these ladies were obviously playing for titles and advantage he had his hour of luxury with them, even though he must pay dearly in the end.

More and more did he come to relish the repose and comfort of the moments he could spend with Nell Gwinn. Rare creature! He could lean on her, trust her, the one woman who loved him for himself; a little like a mother, perhaps, but it flattered him. The beautiful thing about his affair with Nell was that it never grew threadbare.

"Don't let poor Nelly starve!"

Life pursued its everlasting round in Nelly's circle as well. But, as if in envy, death became equally industrious: Mohun, Hart and Lacy, gay companions of her younger years, paid the last toll; her little boy, James, her last gift to the King, taken from her at the moment when he was enriching her latter years with his beauty; her mother whose departure afforded her a huge relief, and finally royal Charles himself dying before he had reached his fifty-fifth year. Meanwhile she lived to the last moment of reckless, extravagant enjoyment. She gave entertainments at her house where she could bring to the notice of her royal guests those of the theatre whom she had known or whose talent she enjoyed advancing; there were lavish banquets, purchases of fabulously expensive jewelry, horses, coaches and sedan-chairs. But that which most seriously disrupted her exchequer was her losses at the basset-table, which gambling contrivance she set up in her own house and which laid her financially by the heels.

At no time did she have much ready cash; her losses were met with I. O. U.'s and bills of indebtedness. She came too uncomfortably close to arrest on various occasions to be at perfect ease, and while never actually imprisoned she was outlawed, after the King's death, for her debt to certain tradespeople, and she acknowledged that "The King's mistresses are accounted ill paymasters."

When she had money, she distributed it with a lavish hand. Her charity was never failing, she interested Charles in her philanthropy and caused him to further her project of a home for aged and crippled soldiers at Chelsea, the corner-stone of which the King himself laid.

Had Charles lived Nelly was to have been made the Countess of Greenwich; as it was she remained plain Nell Gwinn, and as such has been remembered and loved when titles and their owners have become forgotten and meaningless things.

Death removed from her a real lover; hers was the last name on his lips. She had given to the King the best of her life and was full of truth and loyalty to him. He was at once King, companion, friend, lover, the father of her two boys, himself a boy who never quite grew up. No one could succeed him. Other mistresses made vast parade of their grief, hers was too fine to be shared by any one.

Two years were quite long enough to live after the passing of the man who had been dear to her. She lived them in something of the old luxury which thoughtful friends could still supply. King James saw to it that Nelly did not starve.

She had composed a bit of doggerel verse for her tombstone:

"Here Nelly lies, who, thōugh she lived a Slattern,
Yet died a Princess, acting in Saint Cattrin."

It had been a world that was both gay and good, but she was not sorry to leave it. If it had been kind to her she had recompensed it with a like kindness. She had reached heights that no other gutter girl she had ever heard of had touched. The Sovereign of Great Britain and Ireland had given her the most genuine affection of which he was capable.

She peers back into the long ago, past Charles, past Buckhurst—the line grows fainter as it recedes—Lacy, Mohun, Hart, Duncan, past the playhouse to the hovels of Coal Yard Alley and the stews of Lawkenor's Lane. It is very dim. She can scarcely recognize that begrimed, bedraggled, barefoot brat that was once Nell Gwinn. About her are ease and comfort, the solicitude of loving friends and the faithful, sorrowing servitors whom she has remembered generously in her will.

Her eye kindles as she sees her handsome son the founder of a noble line, his blood mingling with the best of Britain. As the shadows gather she murmurs, "He is a King's son!" and smiles in contentment.

The pageant is nearing its close, the end is soon and sudden—apoplexy. She died as she had lived, upon an impulse. The prompter sounds his signal—a bell tinkles in the fly gallery—the curtain unwinds—and she is a memory.

She had lived thirty-eight years.

III

BATH AND JAMES QUIN

III

BATH AND JAMES QUIN

A "City lulled asleep by the chime of the passing years," is Swinburne's description of the town of Bath, and, in truth, "England's Florence" is so old that its beginnings are lost in myth.

During the ninth century, B. C., it was given an immense advertising boom by a Prince of Britain, Bladud, who, after being deported from Court as a leper, turned swineherd and rolled with his pigs in the mud of its springs; returned to royal society completely cured, and became the father of King Lear. Score one for Bath, first factor in the creation of one of the greatest plays ever written!

Here the Romans sought the fountain of youth and built, in A. D. 45, an enduring structure over the warm and healing waters. The fifteenth-century abbey, with its weather-worn angels for ever ascending and descending ladders of crumbly sandstone, speaks of a time when townspeople gave their lives to building, and abbots planted Gothic beauty throughout England.

But Bath, despite its antiquity, persists irrevocably, delightfully Georgian. Its eighteenth-century Royal Pump Room stands triumphant on the old Roman structure, and in the stately Georgian hall Beau Nash, noble of paunch and double of chin, with foot advanced and head thrown back, gazes benignly from his pedestal on the drinkers of a two pennyworth of warm spring water. I had not been astonished had I suddenly heard, from a corner the voices of Doctor Johnson and Sheridan in dispute; or Garrick gibing the pair with witty flings.

The corridors around the central hall of the Pump Room building are lined with framed engravings of eighteenth-century actors, play-bills and manuscript scores of old operas and concerts, for Bath was a music center and many noted composers and conductors directed its orchestra.

Beau Nash was a martinet. His formulæ of social amenities for those frequenting the Pump Room still hang upon its wall, and their strictures applied as well to the patrons of the theatre. It may be judged how much the manners of the time needed discipline when one reads some of the Beau's regulations. He was indefatigable in his insistence upon elegance of deportment and politeness.

Rule 5. "That no gentleman give his ticket to the balls to any but gentlewomen. N. B. Unless he has none of his acquaintance."

Rule 6. "That gentlemen crowding before ladies at the ball show ill manners, and that none do so for the future—except such as respect nobody but themselves."

Rule 7. "That no gentleman or lady take it ill that another dances before them—except such as have no pretense to dance at all."

Rule 9. "That the young ladies take notice how many eyes observe them. N. B. This does not extend to the Have-at-alls."

Rule 10. "That whisperers of lies and scandal be taken for their authors."

One of Nash's chief regulations was the ending of festivities at an early hour. If Bath was to thrive as a health resort, people must early to bed. At eleven o'clock he held up his hand and all music and dancing ceased upon the instant. On one occasion George II's daughter, the Princess Amelia, besought him to allow one dance more, but the Beau's rule was of iron. Amelia might be of royal blood, but he was King of Bath. While the festivities were on, however, he was the life of the party; spirits were not permitted to flag. Once, at a ball, upon overhearing a young lady decline the invitation of a gallant under the plea that, "she did not choose to dance," Nash shouted out, "G—d——n you, Madam! What business have you here if you do not dance?" The affrighted miss tremblingly took her place in the minuet.

Alas! those assembly rooms built for balls and routs, where royalty was entertained, banquets held, political intrigue hatched, fortunes lost or won at high stakes on the gaming tables,—that hall with its paneled walls, its graceful mirrors and chandeliers, now houses a cinema entertainment, and at the entrance I beheld a lurid lithograph of Tom Mix in a Wild West film.

Primarily Bath lured its visitors by the curative waters of the Pump Room, but there were strong counter-attractions in the assembly-room diversions and in the concerts, while for many the real attraction was the theatre. Actors of the provinces, struggling for recognition, often found a welcome here before the autocratic managers of London opened their metropolitan doors. Occasionally one of these magnates would journey to Bath to see an unknown player, the rumor of whose genius had been reported to him. I picked up in a curio shop a brass disk that had been used for admission or "pass-out" purposes. I like to think it has been through the hands of many a spectator who crowded into the pit to applaud the triumph of some of these old actors—Mrs. Siddons, Kean, Macready, Elliston. They all had great nights there.

It is with some reluctance that I leave the assembly rooms and the Pump Room. The ghosts of forgotten perfumes hang about them, and their suggestion of patches, powder, panniers and periwigs is somewhat overpowering. I half expect to see a swaggering red-coated captain arm in arm with a ribboned dandy of the town swing by. But the Abbey waits.

Here the daily service drew a goodly portion of the frivolous society of the eighteenth century. Their perfume must have mingled oddly with the odor of sancity. Whether or no they were attracted by godly pursuit may be judged by these lines from A DESCRIPTION OF BATH, 1734:

"Now for pure worship is the church designed,
O, that the Muse could say to that confin'd!
Eve'n there by meaning looks and cringing bows,
The female Idol her Adorer knows.
Fly hence, Prophane, nor taint this sacred place,
Mock not thy God to flatter Celia's face."

I passed beneath the acrobatic angels of the portal, and soon found myself reading the names of knights, baronets, archbishops and benefactors of the parish on tablets lining the walls and slabs paving the floor.

Here, in the nave, I found Quin. No slab more prominent. I had forgotten that he was buried here, and the discovery gave me a distinct thrill. I recoiled from the lettered stone for I had almost fancied a sepulchral whisper warned me to tread lightly. Quin! The dean of Drury Lane Theatre! The boast of the British stage before Garrick's meteor flashed on London Town. Yet there it was:

HERE LIES THE BODY OF
MR. JAMES QUIN
The scene is chang'd. I am no more.
Death's is the Last Act. Now all is o'er.
R. F.

I am reminded with what kind reverence England has dealt with her departed actors. Among kings, princes, soldiers, scholars and makers of Empire, reposing in the mellow shadows of Westminster Abbey one reads the names of Garrick, Kemble, Sarah Siddons, Barton Booth, Anne Bracegirdle,

Anne Oldfield, Irving and others. Even in Charing Cross Road, within sight of the monument to Edith Cavel, is the statue of Sir Henry Irving, erected to his memory by his fellow players. Throughout England houses in which the illustrious ones of the British stage have lived are marked with tablets. It was doubly pleasant to visit a friend in Half-Moon Street, in London, because in going there I passed the house in which Edmund Kean had dwelt.

James Quin was, in many ways, one of the most striking figures in the long list of favorites of the London theatres. Drama began for him at his birth, for his young mother, after a turbulent matrimonial exploit, was deserted by the harum-scarum fellow who had been her husband. Believing him dead, she again married, this time to a prosperous Irish lawyer, and in 1693 James was born. After many years husband number one turned up, demanded his lawful wife and carried her off. This made little James Quin illegitimate, and he found himself without inheritance, vocation or education. His first experience of the stage was at the Smock Alley Theatre in Dublin, after which he obtained an opening at Drury Lane, acting minor parts with grace, force and discretion. His rise was rapid. By 1719 his *Macbeth, Brutus, Falstaff, Bajazet* and *Sir John Brute* were loudly praised in the coffee-houses and by the general London public.

Adventure dogged his footsteps. Drawn into a dispute with a low-comedian named Bowen for his too free criticism of the latter's performance in THE LIBERTINE, Bowen managed to get the young actor alone in a tavern room and there charged upon him with a sword. Quin defended himself, endeavoring to keep his adversary away; but Bowen was blind with rage and actually ended his own life by rushing upon Quin's rapier. Before he died he took the blame of the affair upon himself, a circumstance that secured the acquittal of Quin at his trial for manslaughter.

His hot Celtic blood got him into constant trouble. He was as full of quarrel as an egg is full of meat. One of his brawls was with Macklin, the Irish actor—the first to redeem *Shylock* from the ranks of low comedy. Nettled by some broadly comic "business" which Macklin unwarrantably introduced when they were together in a scene, Quin hurled a mouthful of the munched apple he was eating into Macklin's face, whereat the latter seized the tragedian and pummeled him into speechlessness. Quin promptly dispatched a challenge, but Macklin apologized. The memory of the affair rankled for years but was finally patched up in a tavern drinking bout following the funeral of a fellow actor, and Macklin carried Quin home to his lodgings on his shoulders, sound asleep.

A player named Williams was so provoked by Quin's treatment of him in a scene of Addison's CATO that he waylaid the tragedian after the play under the arches of Covent Garden and compelled him to a duel. The contest began at once, and before the roused watch could intervene, Williams, run through the body, was lifeless on the ground. Again Quin was acquitted, but it is to his credit that his anguish and remorse never left him. And yet another quarrel with Theophilus Cibber about Cibber's wife. Swords were out and there was slashing of arms and fingers, but this time interference from bystanders prevented a fatal issue.

Doubtless the estimation in which Quin was held as an actor was of great influence in warding off punishment for his brawls. He represented the crowning achievement of the British stage. Many strove to rival him, but none could unseat him from his high place in the public's regard. Ponderous of movement and impressive in manner, he suited in his grandiloquence the taste of the time, giving "true weight and dignity to sentiment by a well regulated tone of voice, judicious elocution and easy deportment." He sang well. One of his successes was *Captain Macheath* in Gay's Beggar's Opera.

His most genuine triumphs according to an old critic were won in "characters of singular humor, of dignified folly, of blunt and boisterous demeanour, of treacherous art, contemptuous spleen and even pleasing gravity." In them none claimed to be his rival. A somewhat different estimate is given by Churchill, the satirist, who evidently disliked his acting: he pilloried the player in a merciless lampoon in the Rosciad, which began:

"His eyes, in gloomy socket taught to roll,
Proclaimed the sullen 'habit of his soul,'
Heavy and phlegmatic he trod the stage,
Too proud for tenderness, too dull for rage."

With Quin's gruffness, irascibility and quick Irish temper, were a sociability and generosity that endeared him to his fellows. No one went empty-handed away from him. He adored the good things of the table, once declaring in praise of his favorite fish, John Dory, that truly to enjoy it, "one should have a gullet from here to the antipodes and a palate all the way." Garrick, who never spared a friend or enemy whom he could make the subject of an epigram or satire, made Quin's gormandizing the burden of a jingle that became popular. He represented the fat player as standing before the tomb of Duke Humphrey at St. Albans and thus soliloquizing:

> "A plague on Egypt's art, I say!
> Embalm the dead? On senseless clay
> Rich wines and spices waste?
> Like sturgeon, or like brawn shall I
> Bound in a priceless pickle lie
> Which I can never taste?
> Let me embalm this flesh of mine
> With turtle fat and Bordeaux wine
> And spoil the Egyptian trade!
> Than good Duke Humphrey happier I,
> Embalmed alive old Quin shall die,
> A mummy ready made."

Quin's wit was perhaps not so polished as Garrick's—but it was ever ready. Well known is his reply to Peg Woffington who, on coming off the stage in male attire as *Sir Harry Wildair,* declared that she knew one-half of the house thought she was a man. "Believe me, my dear," said Quin, "the other half can tell them that you are not." In all his rough jests there was never real malice, and often they covered a true tenderness of heart. There is a story of his discovering an obscure actor named Winston, out of an engagement and lying ill in a Covent Garden lodging-house. He came in with an attendant carrying a decent suit of clothes. "Get up, Dick," he commanded, "and go to rehearsal." The actor dressed himself in the new apparel, bewildered and exceedingly hungry. He was without the price of breakfast. Confiding this fact to his benefactor, Quin replied, "Nay, Dick, you must put your hand in your own pocket now." Winston thought this a sorry joke until he did as he was bade to do, and there he found a ten-pound note.

His habits of self-indulgence were notorious. During his holidays he was wont to make excursions into the country with some lady who became Mrs. Quin for the time being. When his money gave out he would return to London, give the lady a supper at the "Bedford Head," and present her with a substantial token of his appreciation, with some such valedictory as this:

"Madam, for our mutual convenience I have given you the name of Quin for some time past. There is no reason for our carrying on this farce here in town; and now, Madam, give me leave to un-Quin you, and restore you to your own name for the future."

But all was changed when the town was aroused

by the little man who had journeyed down to London from Litchfield with Doctor Johnson. 'Tis said that the pair covered the entire distance with but one horse between them, each walking or riding a stage alternately. Johnson with his doleful tragedy, IRENE, in his wallet and David Garrick with nothing in his but "three half pence and his hopes."

The old order was swept away. In vain Quin and his fellows brought up their heavy batteries of declamation, portentous pauses, and deliberation. "It seemed," wrote Cumberland, "as if a whole century had been stepped over in the passage of a single scene: old things were done away, and a new order was at once brought forth, bright and luminous." Macklin said that "in a half dozen of characters the little fellow secured his immortality," and that the cabal of players against him was "a puff against thunder."

The rumble of the old school grew more feeble, and with Garrick's rise it became moribund. Quin had viewed with dismay the onslaught on ancient traditions of this extraordinary young man who was dubbed "Roscius" by the town. There is infinite pathos and helplessness in his, "If he is right, then I and all the old actors are wrong." It was a trial to Quin's soul when he went to Drury Lane to see his rival's performance of *Othello*. He was in a state of disparaging groans. He compared him to Hogarth's black boy and said to Doctor Hoadley, his box companion, "Here's Pompey, by God! Where's his lamp and tea kettle?"

But Quin could read the writing on the wall. If he was driven into retirement he went with full honors and colors flying, carrying with him to Bath the comfortable fortune he had amassed through a frugality he had practised in spite of his habits of lavish living. His public regretted him, and he left with them the memory of the greatest of all *Falstaffs*. His period of dominance had been long. For twenty years his word had been law in the theatre, and his reign despotic.

But Bath was no St. Helena. The evening of his life was spent in the city of his own choice, and he went there saying he knew "no better city for an old cock to roost in." No doubt he found other fowls of his feather perching there.

Suppose we take a run down to Bath and have a look at Pierrepont Street. I was sure of it! The old fellow is just stepping from his house, Number 3, (next door to the birthplace of "The Maid of Bath," who became the wife of Richard Brinsley Sheridan) for a stroll on the North Parade, and to drop in on Oliver Goldsmith at Number 11. He won't mind if we follow. His carriage is so erect and his appearance so distinguished that at Court he would be taken for nothing less than an ambassador or a prime minister. If the poet is not at home, he continues on to the South Parade where Landor heard "as many nightingales as ever there was in the bowers of Shiraz," and where Doctor Johnson saw "Bath Belles tripping lightly over hot pavements on cork soles and a clear conscience." If the day is

Mr. James Quin in the character of *Falstaff*

fair, and his gouty legs permit, he will walk as far as the Circus—that huge wheel of stately homes which some one described as, "the finest piece of architecture of its kind in Europe." Here he may catch a glimpse of the Earl of Chatham's coach arriving at the statesman's door; or the painter, Gainsborough, at Number 24, with whom, should he not be engaged on one of his famous portraits, he will pass the time of day. Next door to the painter, at Number 22, an urchin of a dozen years is gazing pensively through the window of the ground floor. His face lights up at the sight of the celebrated person passing ponderously along, and the veteran returns him a genial smile, little dreaming that one day that delicate-faced lad would lose his life in America—condemned as a spy. His name is John André.

If a strong east wind is stirring Quin wraps himself more tightly in his greatcoat and muffler and returns, before long, for his glass of curative waters (for does not the pediment of the Pump Room proclaim in letters of gold and characters of Greek that "Water is Best"?) and discourses to his town acquaintance on the glories of Drury Lane and Covent Garden; or, better still, if a visiting company is having an engagement at the theatre, talks shop with his cronies over port and pipes at "The Bull of the Three Tuns." Be niggardly with the port, James, it plays the very devil with your gout! Much better you stick to the waters. Remember what happened last night! Or perhaps you do not remember that you reeled into Lord Chesterfield before the two chairmen managed to stuff your huge body into your sedan-chair.

"Who is that stout gentleman?" inquires his lordship.

"Only Mr. Quin, milord," replies his servant, "going home from the Three Tuns."

"I think," quoth milord, "Mr. Quin is taking one of the three tuns home with him under his waistcoat!"

The belles and beaux no doubt look upon the renowned player with amusement and condescension, while he, in turn, regards them with an easy contempt; he was never of the fashion, in spite of the tale they tell of his attempt to supplant Beau Nash as dictator.

This fop, now, swaggering along, ogling the pedestrians through his quizzing-glass—a very macaroni—who should he be? With vast pretense at solicitude he makes inquiry after Quin's health.

"Famously," growls the glaring actor. "Getting along famously."

"But how distressing to grow old!" persists the fopling. "What would you give to be as young as I am?"

"I would almost be content to be as foolish," says Quin.

If this imposing gentleman in clerical garb just turning the corner from the Terrace Walk should happen to be the noted Bishop Warburton, he will not especially relish an encounter with Mr. Quin.

He will remember that at Mr. Allen's house, not long since, he undertook to set down the actor in an argument concerning the justice of the execution of King Charles, and that Quin, whose mental powers he affected to despise, quite set his reverend head a-spinning with the quickness and the sting of his retort. There is no love lost between them, but Quin will relish the mock deference and sweeping bow he will bestow on the divine and proceed on his way, chuckling.

To the townspeople there is always a greeting; a nod to a shopman, a courtly lift of his hat to a peer's wife, a smile to a pretty miss, and even an exchange of pleasant words with the Bishop of Bath and Wells. To them he is a sweet, kindly old gentleman, and they honor him.

There was, however, a crumbled rose leaf in his bed of ease at Bath: Garrick! The continuous laudation of "Roscius" in London found its way down to him through pamphlet and report. It rankled. Why should Garrick be the only wearer of the laurel? His own were as fresh and worn with a statelier grace. To Rich, the manager of Covent Garden, he dispatched a note; a marvel of suggestion and brevity:

"I am at Bath. Quin."

The answer was immediate and even more to the point:

"Stay there and be damned. Rich."

But it was the true kindliness that lay beneath the rough husk of Quin which, after years of none too cordial relation, won over Garrick. Davey had never been so supremely sure of his eminence as to be free from jealousy. He had unseated Quin, it is true, but Quin had been too long a supreme favorite to lose entirely his popularity, and Garrick frequently writhed under the praise of his rival. Quin "died hard." Indeed after Garrick's complete dominance at Drury Lane had been established, Quin was receiving a thousand pounds a season at Covent Garden—a much larger sum than that paid to "Roscius," and the largest, at that time, that had ever been paid to an English actor for a season's service. But no one could for ever remain Quin's enemy, and doubtless in his retirement he ceased to look formidable to Garrick. Their friendship became so well established that Quin was a guest at Garrick's house at Hampton when he was stricken with his fatal illness.

For nearly a year he is fighting for his life at his home in Bath. He is not afraid, for the habit of the warrior is strong, and his marvelous constitution defies the Reaper. Hosts of his old friends, and even his enemies, hasten down from London to sit at his bedside and listen to the lively stories he never tires of telling. Every morning his door is the scene of inquiries of the good people of Bath, anxious to know how Mr. Quin fares to-day. His poise and self-control now never leave him.

To-night he seems drowsy and not inclined to

much talk. A friend or two speak quietly in the shrouded light of the chamber. In a corner the doctors are discussing his condition.

"I don't like the rise in his temperature. His skin is too dry. If we could only make him sweat."

Quin half opens his eyes, and beckons them over with a feeble wave of the hand on the coverlid. "What's that you said about me?" he asks.

"We think that if we could give you something to make you sweat, 'twould be a relief to you."

There is a pause; then a slight smile on Quin's face. "Gad'szooks! That's easy enough! Send in your bills and it's done!"

Presently he says he is hungry. What could he not do to a breakfast of John Dory and claret if he were well! "I've often wished my mouth were as large as the center arch of Westminster Bridge and that the river ran claret." A few sips of his gruel and some brandy are all he can swallow, but he brightens. They are speaking of George III. He has that week delivered his speech in Parliament.

"Did he do it well?" queries the sick man.

Excellently well, they tell him.

"I knew he would!" Quin exclaims. "It was I who taught the boy to speak. Frederick, Prince of Wales, appointed me instructor to the young princes and princesses in elocution, and they appeared in plays at Leicester House under my direction, gentlemen." And he adds with pride that the King had not been ungrateful. He had placed his old master's name as beneficiary on the civil list.

Some one speaks of angling. "A cruel sport, gentleman," says Quin. "Suppose, now, a being as much my superior as I am to those poor fish were to say, 'Tis a fine evening, I'll go Quinning! If he were to bait his hook with a haunch of venison I should gorge. And how should I like to be dragged from Richmond to Kingston floundering and flouncing with a hook in my gullet?"

This has been a long speech: too long. He laughs a little at his own fantasy, then sinks back in his pillows with a little sigh.

Now his wits begin to wander. Broken speeches from *Cato* and *Sir John Brute* come from his lips. He is back on the stage of Old Drury, acting to an enraptured throng. "Hark at them;" he murmurs, "how they applaud!" His voice trails away into silence and he sleeps. His breathing is very light.

Toward morning he wakes. "I wish," he says in a voice still distinct and with a faint echo of the music that rang in the tones of his *Macbeth*, his *Bajazet* and his *Cato*. "I could wish that this last tragic scene were over, and I hope that I may be able to meet and pass through it with dignity."

Did King Charles say a finer thing than that? Did his, "Gentlemen, I fear I am an unconscionable time a-dying" speak a greater bravery and courtesy on the threshold of the dark portal? I vow not.

To-morrow or the next day his will is to be read, and we shall learn something even finer about this rough, caustic duelist, actor, humorist and epicure, something of his benevolence and kindness of heart.

No one who has ever had a claim to his friendship has been forgot, and the list is an exceedingly long one. To an individual whom he did not like he bequeaths his watch, "in accordance with an imprudent promise."

Garrick owed him the eloquent tribute of the epitaph in the Abbey. The tablet is in the wall which separates the choir from the left aisle. Beneath the sculptured face of the actor, round and assertive in its canopy of a full ringletted wig, one reads the lines:

"That tongue which set the table on a roar
And charmed the public ear is heard no more:
Closed are those eyes, the harbingers of wit,
Which spake before this tongue, what SHAKESPEARE
writ:
Cold is that hand, which living was stretched forth
At friendship's call to succor modest worth:
Here lies JAMES QUIN: deign reader to be taught,
What e'er thy strength of body, force of thought,
In nature's happiest mould however cast,
To this complexion thou must come at last.
"D. GARRICK.

"AETAT LXXIII.
Obit M.D.CCLXVI."

Was David sincere? Let us hope so. He could well afford to be!

IV

THE VARIED ADVENTURES OF BELLAMY THE BEAUTIFUL

IV

THE VARIED ADVENTURES OF BELLAMY THE BEAUTIFUL

THE grace, witchery and comeliness that were acquired by the fair and frail George Anne Bellamy in the golden summer of her beauty were not foreshadowed in the features of the unpleasant-looking brat who was taken to her mother's London lodgings a few years after that lady had brought into being this love-child of the British ambassador to Portugal, Lord Tyrawley.

The visit was the inspiration of the child's nurse. She had seen Mrs. Bellamy's name on the play-bill posted at the portal of Covent Garden Theatre and could fancy no greater joy than that of witnessing the meeting of mother and daughter.

George Anne, overwhelmed with the sight of the sweet-faced lady in genteel garments standing before her, ran forward with a rapturous, "Mamma!" There was no welcoming embrace. She felt herself rudely shoved off, and the message of mother love that greeted her was, "My God! what have you brought me here? This goggle-eyed, splatter-faced, gabbart-mouthed wretch is not my child. Take her away!"

Yet this object of parental loathing was destined to reign jointly with her sister queens of Drury

Lane and Covent Garden for three decades. In the clubs, the coffee-houses, the drawing-rooms, at the balls and routs her whims, her amours, her extravagant entertainments and her latest escapades were bandied to and fro as the newest town gossip. Money was thrown at her feet only to be tossed in the air. Men fought for her, went mad for her, loathed her, adored her. With most of them she went down to ruin, playing the game to its end: a debtor's prison, an ocean of tears, a clamor of lamentations and anon a renewed George Anne, more feline, fascinating, irresistible and saucily seductive emerges from the wreck of yesteryear. There are willing victims waiting for betrayal; nightly they see her pouring passionate though stilted blank verse upon her stage lovers, to whose embraces she yields with stately grace, and profess themselves ready to die for one kiss from those ripe lips. To be pillowed upon a breast yielding as softest moss, whiter than snow, to gaze into eyes of Heaven's blue! Could death be sweeter?

Says Doran: "When she played some lady distraught through affection the stoutest hearts under embroidered waistcoats crumbled away, often into inconceivable mountains of gold dust."

Her career was a catalogue of startling episodes, her very birth an adventure. Had not the Quaker-born Miss Seal hurried away in pique at Lord Tyrawley's treachery and indifference it would have taken place in Lisbon. As it was she sailed for Ireland in 1731 on Captain Bellamy's ship, married him, and when, a couple of months later in Dublin, little George Anne came tumbling into the world the occasion was one of such complete astonishment to the good Captain that he could only gasp and splutter in incoherent rage. A cuckold even on his wedding-day! 'Twas not to be endured. Incontinent and indecent flight was his only resource. He disappeared, never to return, but leaving behind the ringing and respectable name of Bellamy to be borne by the child that was none of his.

Finding no joy in the motherhood of a daughter who was merely a reminder of her bitter heartbreak the deserted Ariadne gave her to a military captain, and little Anne's lullabies were the taps and bugle calls of a Dublin barracks.

But if Mrs. Bellamy did not take pride in her offspring Lord Tyrawley did. The gay dog returned from his Lisbon ambassadorship bringing a Portuguese mistress and a brood of children each of them by a *different mother*. His lordship's house at Bushy Park resembled, according to Anne's account, a Turkish seraglio; here she found herself in company with three half-sisters, her semi-detached brothers having been packed off to school at Mary-le-Bone.

Meanwhile life had been moving eventfully with Anne. At Tyrawley's request she had been sent to France to be educated in the Convent of the Nunciats at Boulogne. She had been there but a brief term when one morning the convent seethed with excitement—groups of nuns were hurrying to and fro—cries of anguish rent the air. A sister had been detected in the act of shattering her vow of chastity and was condemned to a horrible end. Before the eyes of the terrified little English girl the hapless victim was placed against the wall and brick by brick, remorselessly and deliberately she was immured alive. Frantic, almost insane, Anne begged to be removed from a place of such hideous practise and succeeded in being transferred to the care of the Ursulines where the kindlier sisters ministered to her bodily and mental growth. When she arrived at the age of eleven she recrossed the Channel, her young brain burnished with convent culture and sifted over with a smattering of classic writings and a few foreign phrases. Established in the shop of a peruquier in St. James Street, London, a former domestic in Tyrawley's household, she waited his lordship's return from Portugal with his assortment of offspring.

Nothing could be tenderer than Lord Tyrawley's reception of her. He was charmed—so was she. It was then that she found herself a bright star in the Bushy Park seraglio, much to the disgust of the dusky beauty whom Lord Tyrawley had brought from Lisbon to soothe his moments of dalliance, and who had jealously-guarded children of her own.

Followed happy days and nights at Bushy and in London, visits from Pope of Twickenham, the Earl of Chesterfield and Richard Brinsley Sheridan, the flash of brilliant talk, the scandalmongering of belles and beaux; George II was on the throne and society was gay and garrulous. In this atmosphere George Anne grew apace, acquired grace and beauty and learned to simper at the innuendoes and coarse compliments of the macaronis who fluttered about her and laughed at her convent-bred manners.

In the turn of the kaleidoscope she met Rich, the uncouth but canny manager then struggling with the none too swelling fortunes of Covent Garden Theatre, became acquainted with his family—and played at being grown-up actors with his daughters. They learned the parts of OTHELLO with our little lady as the *Moor*.

Says George Anne: "As I was raving in all the extremity of jealous madness Mr. Rich accidentally passed by the room in which we were rehearsing. Attracted by the powerful sweetness of the *Moor's* voice, which he declared to be superior to any he had ever heard, he listened without interrupting our performance; but as soon as it was concluded he entered the room and paid me a thousand compliments on my theatrical abilities. Among other things he said that in his opinion I should make one of the first actresses in the world, adding that if I could turn my thoughts to the stage he should be happy to engage me."

Elate with this praise Anne flew to her own mother who promptly threw cold water on her daughter's sudden ardor.

"I am altogether averse to it," she said, "for I know full well the temptations and the disadvantages attendant on a theatrical life."

Rich was persistent and at length Mrs. Bellamy consented.

Rich was not without wisdom, the drama was growing hoary at Covent Garden. Mistresses Horton, Clive and Pritchard, noble wheel-horses of the theatre, were upholding its traditions with all their might and majesty, but their charms were becoming something musty, while at the rival house Garrick held popular favor easily in hand assisted by the sprightly Peg Woffington and the luscious Mrs. Cibber. Beauty and new blood were needed at Covent Garden—here it was and young enough in all conscience—only fourteen, Anne said! Rich cautiously broached the idea to old Quin, the most capital performer at his theatre. Quin governed the playhouse with a rod of iron; Rich, though proprietor, had through his slipshod methods dwindled to a mere cipher.

Quin swung his Falstaffian bulk and looked down over his fat cheeks and various chins at the young thing before him.

"What! play *Chamont* to that chit of a girl's *Monimia?* Egad! you'll be bringing me nursing babes to act with next. Are ye aware that THE ORPHAN is a tragedy, not a farce?"

For once in his life Rich was firm.

"Curse my vitals!" shouted Quin, "if ye persist I'll publicly declare my sentiments on this outrage. I'll attend no rehearsals. Ye can take that from me."

He stormed out of the theatre, and kept his word.

The two actors who were to play *Castalio* and *Polydore, Monimia's* lovers, followed Quin's example and were heavily fined for their action by Rich. Brought to their senses by the manager's severity they appeared next morning and facetiously mumbled and whistled through their speeches. But not Quin, the old Achilles sulked in his tent. Almost the entire company openly jeered at the manager's upstart, spouting through *Monimia's* lines.

Rich stuck to his guns; he even sent George Anne to a mercers for a new costume instead of the customary cast-off garment of some lady of quality supplied to the young brides and virgins in his plays, empresses and queens being confined to black velvet. The players very nearly broke into rebellion, the report of which went beyond the walls of the theatre, and the public became interested.

The night of the performance of THE ORPHAN arrives, the theatre holds an audience larger than it has housed for many a night. Gossip has been bruited through the town concerning Rich's new prodigy and the row she has created among the Covent Garden players. Pit and boxes are buzzing with stories about her.

Before the curtain rises the effrontery that has kept her in countenance throughout the stormy rehearsals falls from her, her heart beats wildly beneath the bodice of her dazzling new robes. Her entrance cue is spoken, but she stands frozen in the wings until the prompter gives her a push and George Anne almost stumbles into the blaze of lights. Suffocating she remains speechless, blinking at the vague mass of something that is an audience and which is bestowing plaudits upon her. She can not remember her lines of *Monimia*, and the prompter's repetition of them falls on closed ears. But for the charming picture of the dainty child in her lovely gown standing dumb and helpless before them the spectators would have laughed her from the stage had not the bell-wether of the pit, Mr. Chitty, risen from his seat, demanded silence and ordered the curtain dropped.

Quin exults. "By Gad! Rich, you've brought this on yourself. You would pick the little beggar to affront me. And I'm supposed to be her brother in this play. Look at her! Ha!"

Rich entreats her, "Don't let them distract you, girl, you'll have them at your feet yet. Exert yourself."

The scene recommences. The bewildered novice is finding voice now, but it is so weak and choked that it can scarcely be heard at the side boxes. Applause, half derisive, half sympathetic adds to the absurdity of the situation. Quin grins and snorts without disguise in his scenes with her.

Rich's claque spread in different parts of the house can make no headway.

The act ends in confusion. Rich is fairly tearing his wig. On through the succeeding scenes little Bellamy wavers and reels like a baited rat in a pit until the fourth act. Let Anne tell the story:

"This was the critical period which was to determine my fate, by this criterion was I, as an actress, to rise or fall. When, to the astonishment of the audience, the surprise of the performers and the exultation of the manager I felt myself suddenly inspired. I blazed out at once with meridian splendor, and I acquitted myself throughout the whole of this most arduous part of the character, in which even many veterans have failed, with the greatest eclat. Mr. Quin was so fascinated by this unexpected exertion that he waited behind the scenes until the conclusion of the act, when, lifting me up from the ground in a transport, he exclaimed, 'Thou art a divine creature and the true spirit is in thee.' The audience likewise honored me with marks of their approbation. The performers who, half an hour before, had looked upon me as an object of pity, now crowded around me with compliments of gratulation. And Mr. Quin, in order to compensate for the contempt with which he had treated me, was warmer, if possible, in his eulogiums than he had been in his sarcasms."

This was the beginning of the public career of George Anne Bellamy. Her popularity began from that moment. Business at Covent Garden mounted appreciably—the town had a new toy.

There were *petit soupers* at James Quin's house—where, completely won, he assumed the rôle of counselor and friend of the new beauty. Knowing the old reprobate as we do I think we may suspect him of something more than a fatherly affection. Among the wits and gallants of the town Anne learned to pose tremendously. No fine lady could more graciously extend her hand to be kissed or hide her face with her fan at a ribald jest with a more modish air.

Among her flatterers was Lord Byron—great-uncle to the poet, an earlier profligate of the family with little to commend him beyond his title and good looks. The Bellamy's rejection of his addresses only inflamed him the more. Together with a titled but infamous pander he conspired to abduct and ruin her. By a ruse he lured her from her house to a quiet street where Anne suddenly found herself hoisted into a waiting coach, and his lordship and his friend set scampering off with their victim to the edge of London.

Facing the fields at the top of North Audley Street was a lonely house where the two scheming noblemen deposited the protesting little creature and left her with dire imprecations on her head if she did not yield. Providence, however, in the shape of the actress' brother intervened; he got wind of the assault, followed the eloping coach and rescued his sister after having administered a sound thrashing to Lord Byron.

Nevertheless he refused to believe her guiltless. The world of London, which in the Georgian era had many of the characteristics of a country village, followed suit, and with Pecksniffian pusillanimousness turned its aristocratic nose up at her. Discredit shouted at poor Anne from every door formerly flung wide to her. In vain she protested her innocence of the least depravity of the kind imputed to her, everything that ill-nature could suggest was lavishly flung in her face, the scandal sheets paragraphed her, and her mother, forgetful of her own none-too-puritanical past, returned her offspring's letters unopened. Whichever way she looked she saw despair. In her loneliness she turned to her convent textbooks and thought deeply about Adam and Eve.

"Alas!" she reflected, "we see on the very first page of history a memorable instance of the instability of human happiness in the fate of the first created pair. From the never ceasing and inexpressible joys of paradise where every wish was anticipated and pleasures, real and lasting, grew spontaneously did our great progenitors find themselves driven into a world of care, affliction and uncertainty." She hadn't the courage to face the debacle—she fled into the country to some Quaker relatives of her mother, hoping that far from London ill-fame would not follow her.

Perhaps these simple people had never heard of racy doings in London Town—perhaps they had never even heard of her being an actress. They had been made custodians of a legacy of three hundred pounds bequeathed by a cousin to George Anne on condition that she never went on the stage.

Instinctive artist that she was she made up carefully for her part. Nothing could have been simpler or neater than her attire which admitted to her gray gown the addition of ribbands, laces and gauzes. These Clarke relatives were of the denomination known as *wet* Quakers. Anne disclaims any real intention to deceive but—the artful minx!—I can't trust her.

At Clarke Hall in Essex peace really came to her hurt mind, she was warmly received and her heart went out to these apparently sincere, cleanly people.

Still she is not without her reservations. "Have not many instances," she says, "fallen within your observation where a broad-brimmed hat and sad-colored coat, or a green apron and plain linen have covered a prouder heart than all the gay pomp of a birthday suit?" She kept these observations to herself and allowed her demure manners to win their way—an easy conquest.

The Clarkes think she has come to collect her legacy and they pay her a much needed sum in the shape of interest on it.

Disguising her eagerness Anne murmurs her thanks. "It is generous in you, and I accept with gratitude, but such is not the purpose of my visit. It is that after a distressing illness in London I may seek the quiet and healing air of a country life." Indeed her pallid face bears evidence that she speaks with sincerity.

After a few weeks of blessed respite had turned to boredom she missed the customary adulation of her beauty and charms.

Her instinctive coquetry ensnared the susceptibility of the village apothecary, he became wholly enslaved and proposed for her hand. As he was a good Quaker the Clarkes aided and abetted his suit. This was not exactly the result that gratified the artful little lady.

London was calling loudly. She returned to it earlier than she anticipated, but not in the manner she had looked for. A fine gentleman, Mr. Moore, *au courant* with town affairs, came for a neighborly call and on being presented recognized something strangely familiar about the face and figure in the sad-colored gown.

His astonishment was so great that he unthinkingly burst out with: "A wet Quaker indeed! It is Miss Bellamy, the celebrated actress who met with so much applause last winter at Covent Garden Theatre."

Anne's shrewd suspicions of the treachery of Quaker calmness were instantly verified. Mrs. Clarke, no longer a Quaker, became Xanthippe.

"Avaunt!" she cried. "Thou art a child of iniquity—thou hast sold thyself to the impure one—thou art an impostress!"

Anne denies the accusation with spirit—she has never meant to deceive—she has never uttered a falsehood in her life. Mrs. Clarke is somewhat mollified—almost relenting, when Mr. Clarke, who had drawn Mr. Moore aside and learned the true story, returned and indignantly proposed to return to town.

"Nothing shall prevent my going to the great city to make that bad man do her justice by taking her for his spouse!"

Thereat his wife's rage rekindled.

"Avaunt!" she shrieked again. "Thou comest, with all thy frauds to seduce my best-loved; Satan hath got hold of thee, perdition will follow thee! Leave my mansion!"

Anne thought herself back on the stage of Covent Garden Theatre; it was dear old Mrs. Pritchard declaiming an outburst from an Otway tragedy.

The absurd situation reached its anticlimax. It truly couldn't last. The Quaker Xanthippe softened at the end and gave her improving books, admonitions and a little money—enough to keep body and soul together a while longer. It was time to go, but she dared not return to town so soon.

An acquaintance in the near-by village of Ingatestone gave her the excuse for a visit, but arriving at the mansion she found the family absent and was forced to put up at an inn where she was viewed with some suspicion, later finding shelter with a farmer's wife, and in the tranquillity of the place her troubles abated. But her peace of mind could not be coaxed back—no word from her mother. Several weeks had passed when returning to the farmhouse from a solitary stroll among the lanes and green hedges she found herself clasped in her mother's arms. There was a happy evening, and far into the night there was much to explain, discuss and forgive. The following morning the recitation of the latest town tattle, the recent doings at the theatres, and the sight of some new modish gowns set all her delight in bucolic simplicity flying. Nothing but London and a return to the stage for her now, she was a fool ever to have left them.

"My resolution was no sooner formed than the calm retreat I had been so fond of grew irksome.

Rural walks, moss-grown seats, spreading trees, books and contemplation—the prospects I had so often viewed with rapture—the wholesome viands, fresh gathered fruits, nut-brown ale, the hearty welcome, the cheerful gibe and all the pleasures of a rustic table were now distasteful to me."

Nevertheless as the coach conveyed mother and daughter up to town panic took possession of her, the cheek naturally rouged by soft air, sunshine and country living paled as she inhaled the smoke and reek of London.

Could she face it all?

She went into hiding in a rose-embowered suburban cottage and waited impatiently for the return of her mother whom she sent to Rich to tell him that the prodigal daughter had come back.

Mrs. Bellamy's interview with the manager was a little disappointing. The success of scandal that enhances box-office takings in the theatre of our time was unknown to the Georgian play houses. There was scandal enough, heaven knows! Society reeked with it and the stage supplied more than its share, but etiquette ruled it under cover where it could be ogled through quizzing glasses, hinted between the tappings of snuff-boxes and whispered behind fans.

The victim of an affair with a man of title flaunted her brocades behind the footlights at the peril of the town's derision. Anne had simply made the mistake of being found out—guilty or innocent—the worst was believed of the Byron episode. Rich was sympathetic but too shrewd to imperil the business at Covent Garden.

There was, however, a way out of the coil that affairs were in; Richard Brinsley Sheridan was in London raising recruits for his Smock Alley Theatre in Dublin.

"There's the chance for your girl, Mistress Bellamy. She'll get the fine parts and the instruction of a great master. I couldn't do so well as that by her at my theatre."

She left London without taking leave of any one.

"My heart upbraided me for my ingratitude in not paying my respects to Mr. Rich and to Mr. Quin, gentlemen to whom I lay under such great and numerous obligations, but I could not so far overcome my bashful timidity as to do it."

As the chimes of Bow Bells grew fainter, as the four turrets of the Tower and Wren's swelling dome of St. Paul's were blurred by the smoke of London, Anne's spirits rose. She looked about her. It was a somewhat motley crew that Sheridan had collected to delight his Dublin patrons. He carried his leadership with an air and fed their imaginations with the glory and fame that waited them in the Irish capital. His wit sparkled and his blarney was unceasing.

"Ye'll never know what favor is until ye come into the glow of the foots at the Smock Alley Theatre."

For a day or two he kept them company then

posted ahead to prepare their reception at Dublin, leaving them to wend their way by post and horseback over the mountains of Wales.

It was a rare excursion for them all. Sheridan had franked the expense of their travel and they could give themselves to complete irresponsibility. Freshets, mountain storms, coach break-downs, lamed horses were but sources of laughter. Once they arrived at an inn drenched to their bones with a downpour.

A fellow traveler, Mr. Crump, who had become hopelessly entangled in George Anne's bewildering net of graces, saw his opportunity for an adventure. He commandeered the best room and ordered refreshments. Anne found a fire blazing on the hearth when, with dried garments, she entered at his urgent invitation. His mode of attack was quite his own, alternately simpering and scowling and prancing about the room. He approached his divinity and with a deep sigh, which Anne said "would have blown the boat we had lately entered over the river without the assistance of the ferryman," took her hand.

"My dear Miss Bellamy," he demanded, "answer me one question—were you ever in love?"

"Oh, yes, violently."

"And you are really attached?"

"For ever!"

"Would it be deemed impertinent were I to presume to ask with whom?"

"Surely it can be of no consequence to you, but

if it will gratify your curiosity, it is with myself—I am a female Narcissus.''

Further attempts of the Machiavellian Mr. Crump were checked by the arrival of the rest of the players. The gentleman retired in confusion leaving his costly supper to be devoured by the famished Thespians. Hollyhead was reached almost at the moment that the packet was spreading her sails. Anne fell asleep and knew nothing until she heard the cry, ''The Hill of Howth!''

Sheridan had not exaggerated the warmth of hospitality that was extended to Mistress Bellamy, nor was the admiration of her work in the theatre voiced in uncertain terms. Society took her up, it knew nothing of the tarnish attached to her name in London. Lord Tyrawley's sister, Mrs. O'Hara, introduced her everywhere as her niece, the honorable Mrs. Butler extended her social prestige. To add to the success of the season Garrick arrived to appear in his favorite characters for his friend, Sheridan. KING JOHN was announced for the first performance and Sheridan cast George Anne for *Queen Constance.*

Garrick demurred.

''Damme! Sheridan, she's too young for *Constance,* let her play *Prince Arthur.*''

Sheridan was insistent.

The impertinent Anne broke the impasse by declaring that she would not appear at all, and pranced off to lay her woes before the powerful Mrs. Butler, demanding that Garrick be taught a lesson.

That lady immediately issued her ukase that society should abstain from attending the performance of King John, and society did as it was told.

To add to Roscius' humiliation the play was later repeated and Anne had her way—she appeared as *Constance*.

Garrick met with a further rebuff when he proposed, for the Bellamy's benefit, that she play the name part in *Jane Shore*.

"No, Mr. Garrick," the minx replied, "if I am too young for *Constance* I am too young for *Jane Shore*."

David tried to wheedle her into acceptance, he wrote her an endearing epistle beginning with, "My soul's idol, the most beautified Ophelia," which, to Garrick's mortification, got into the public print. It was not without some relief that, when his engagement ended, he took his way back to London.

Anne deserves a thrashing—insolent little baggage!—but she has piqued the interest of the great Roscius. In subsequent years at Garrick's Drury Lane Theatre she is destined to profit by her impertinence.

The season of 1745 was gay. Ireland was always a land of lovers, they swarmed about the new beauty. One of them, a Mr. Medlicote, quite nosed out of the circle of her admirers, caused it to be rumored that he had been the recipient of her favors. Once more scandal reared its head and threatened to devour the thoughtless coquette; even her patroness, Mrs. Butler, lifted her aristocratic eyebrows and publicly snubbed her. Her downfall was short lived, however; brought to book her traducer acknowledged that he had never spoken to her—never seen her, otherwise than in her play-acting at Smock Alley Theatre.

Reinstated Anne raised her demure eyes at the attempted assassin of her fair fame and pronounced him good to look upon.

"How much more charming and accomplished would he have been," she wrote, "had truth spread her refulgent beams over those perfections which nature in so bounteous a manner had favored him! The venom of the tongue is more fatal in its consequences than the poison of the asp. Alas! the generality of mankind seems to comprise every virtue in that of chastity. Without doubt chastity is one of the first and most admired virtues that adorns the female mind, yet when we consider that punishment certainly attends a breach of that virtue, and that disgrace is their consequent portion, surely the truly virtuous ought rather to pity and pour balm into the bosom of those who are thus unfortunately condemned to an earthly purgatory, and have many extenuations to plead, than add to their afflictions by reproaches or contempt."

Thus Anne the Moralist in her best copy-book manner, writing her Apology during her maturer years when she had cause to repent her own many excursions from the straight and narrow way.

All was not fair weather with affairs in Smock Alley during the second season, increasing indifference of the public, clashes with rowdy bucks in his theatre, desertions from his company and the growing popularity of the opposition house in Crow Street strewed troubles aplenty in Sheridan's path.

Anne was wearying, London was calling again and she heard its voice. Her adieus must be said.

She had grown in skill, reputation and the power to manipulate her charms upon the stage. She yearned for a bigger field. Her admirers voiced their lament at her departure. One of them burst into ecstatic rhyme on her *Belvidera* in his farewell:

"Hail, child of Nature and the pride of Art!
Equally form'd to glad and pain the heart.
Thro' various passions you accomplish'd shine,
Your looks expressive speak the coming line.
Adored while living, with applause you die;
Each judge beholds you with a Jaffier's eye."

There was no engagement waiting Anne in London—the season was dead, Rich in the country, Quin, recuperating from overeating and drinking, was cleansing his vast system with the healing waters of Bath and she had, a year previously, declined an offer of ten pounds a week that Garrick had made her for Drury Lane. But there wasn't a vestige of the old cloud of disrepute that had enveloped her—how long ago was it? It didn't matter, the public's memory was short, and she was happy and confident.

With the opening of Covent Garden Theatre her name was in the list of performers—so was that of Woffington. The pair were predestined to become deadly rivals, they cordially hated each other at their first meeting.

At the moment of that meeting Margaret Woffington was in the zenith of her glory, her public adored her. Her lovers were many and among them was the accomplished Garrick with whom she lived, without benefit of the clergy, in an establishment kept in financial well-being by mutual agreement in the ratio of fifty-fifty.

Often they spat over household expenditures: Garrick's infatuation did not blind him to purse leakages: Davy counted his pennies, Peg scattered hers to the winds, true daughter of Erin that she was. One month's management of the ménage was Garrick's, the following Woffington's.

"Isn't this tea stronger than common?" asked a guest at a house party. "It's as red as blood."

"Right! This is Peggy's month."

Others of her slave troop were not so parsimonious. When she died at the age of forty after a long illness she was amply protected. Hogarth painted her lying in her bed of sickness—mob-capped and still beautiful.

Her beauty was combined with a talent beyond the range of Bellamy's, and Bellamy knew it to her cancerous envy. Her versatility was exceptional, her range of parts reached from *Ophelia* to the hoydens and hell-rakes of Restoration comedy. She hid her comely Irish face under painted wrinkles for old women and blossomed into the most bewitching creature alive in the "breeches parts," exposing a leg that was the despair of every young buck of the town. Her *Sir Harry Wildair* was pronounced superior to Garrick's.

"A bad actress," croaked Walpole, "but she has spirit." Indeed she had something more than that—a roguish gray eye, a hot temper always lapsing into unfailing good nature, a bitter tongue, a ready sympathy, impulsive generosity, a voice musical in spite of its harshness, alternately an angel and a hell-cat, one moment aflame, the next a limpid rivulet of laughter: of such was Margaret Woffington.

Small wonder that Anne ate her foolish little heart out! When Woffington played *Jocasta,* George Anne, acting opposite her, was overcome by the withering fire of her scorn and fury and swooned away in the scene.

Faintings, suffocations, megrims and vapors were fashionable in the days of the Royal Georges and very effective guns in the store of Anne's artillery.

The year of Woffington's death brought the third of the house of Hanover to the throne of England.

By this time George Anne had seen her mother well bestowed. That lady had turned Methodist and had grown a very model of prim propriety; finding the licentious social set intolerable she devoted herself to prayers, to constant raids upon her daughter's pay envelope, and to the society of her household pets: cats, dogs and monkeys. Her apartment at Somerset House was filled with yelping dogs and loose monkeys dressed in regimentals or as fine ladies and gentlemen.

Anne was winning her way into high prominence,

a seductive helplessness and cloying sweetness in her performance of persecuted heroines reinforcing a beauty that completely enthralled the patrons of the playhouse; she had something of the appealing quality of a Bernhardt or a Duse. In a sob-compelling piece called CLEONE, by Dodsley, in which she subsequently acted, she flooded the stage and the spectators with tears; of these amazing nights of unrestrained grief at Covent Garden the poet Gray wrote: "The people are going in droves to the theatre and confessing their joy because they *cried so!*"

Beaux flocked to the greenroom to pay court to her, they swarmed about the stage entrance, and the utmost care and circumspection was necessary for the safe conduct of her sedan-chair to her lodgings lest it be assaulted. A French actor, Mouet, advised her to go to Paris where he assured her she would fascinate the Grand Monarque; with dreams of becoming a second Madame de Maintenon, Anne seriously considered making the journey.

But the nights of special attraction were those when she and Woffington were cast in the same bill—anything might happen on the stage when the rival beauties came together in their scenes—danger threatened if they had lethal weapons in their hands. As *Roxana* and *Statira,* the rival queens in Lee's ALEXANDER, they bore daggers, and never were ladies more inclined to use them in downright earnest than these stage sovereigns. Wagers upon the outcome of the encounters were sometimes made by the members of the company who crowded the wings to watch them. Attired in the newest Paris creations, all stays and hoops and farthingales, frills and furbelows and towering head-dresses, they enacted the Roman matrons of this play. Each successive presentation brought a new jewel, ribbon or ornament to the costume of either *Roxana* or *Statira.* One night the gorgeousness of Bellamy's gown wrought Woffington into a fit of fury; it was rumored that her dagger's customary dull point had been purposely sharpened. Whether this were true or no, Peg hurled herself with unwonted savagery upon her rival—a shriek and the act ended in confusion. When the curtain fell blank verse gave place to Billingsgate—there was real need for interposition.

"You dirty vixen!" shouted Woffington. "Small wonder you can plume yourself like a peacock when your minister, Henry Fox, supplies the feathers."

"Why don't you do the same?" retorted the undaunted Bellamy. "Are your paramours too stingy? You have half the town to draw upon!"

It is not an easy task to obtain a wholly accurate estimate of George Anne's deeds and motives in her career apart from the theatre; her APOLOGY, though written in the form of personal letters to an anonymous recipient, is intended for the public eye, indeed she says so with naïve frankness, and that it shall contain nothing but real facts: "I once more assure you that truth shall guide my pen through every page." But the amazing little lady is overwhelmed with the sense of her own charm and fascination and is hopelessly romantic. Each affair of the heart which she has—and they are countless—ends in disaster and sorrow. She swoons away in the magnitude of her emotions, thereafter taking to her bed with a wasting illness which keeps her from the theatre for many nights.

Men woo her, win her and forsake her. In the list of her friendships, amorous and otherwise, one finds General Braddock whose name is written large, together with that of George Washington, in the records of the French and Indian Wars.

"General Braddock," she writes, "to whom I had been known from my infancy and who was particularly fond of me was about to go to America. While he was making preparations for his voyage he was more frequently than usual at our house. The evening before his departure he supped with me, accompanied by his two aids-de-camp, Major Burton and Captain Orme. Before we parted the General told me he should never see me more, for he was going with a handful of men to conquer whole nations, and to do this they must cut their way through unknown woods. He produced a map of the country saying at the same time, 'Dear Pop, we are sent like sacrifices to the altar.' The event of the expedition too fatally verified the General's expectations. On going away he put into my hands a paper which proved to be his will."

Were there days on the march when Braddock's thoughts turned back to that pleasant evening? And while the nightly camp-fire reddened the forest trees around Fort Duquesne, and the outposts strained their eyes through the dark for sign of their Indian foes, were there tales of the gaiety of London Town, and did the General tell Lieutenant George Washington about a certain fascinating little hussy there called George Anne Bellamy? Who knows?

The melancholy wooer at the Welsh inn, Mr. Crump, whose artful designs upon the young actress on her way to Dublin were so ignominiously defeated, had never quite lost sight of her nor she of him. Crump had kept true to one purpose, to marry George Anne. He laid siege to Anne's mother and made known his passion to Lord Tyrawley, both of whom favored his suit. But she would have none of him. Lord Byron, whose abortive attempt upon her in the past had met with disaster, and who had no idea whatever of marriage, forgot his humiliation and swore to Manager Rich that he would carry off his treasure. Anne would have none of him, either. A new god of idolatry had been set up—Sir George Metham.

Metham was one of the squadron of regular Bellamyites who never missed a performance of hers at Covent Garden Theatre, but he had hitherto been singled out for no special favor until the evening when she played *Lady Froth* in THE DOUBLE DEALER with Quin and Woffington. She had been successful, the audience had bestowed liberal plaudits upon her, and she wore a pretty new dress. Sir George pushed his way through the throng of ogling dandies in the greenroom. Anne, elate and all a-whimper with her triumph, saw him and, as she says: "A blush of crimson threw its veil over my face." She shot a hot glance at the poor young man, sending him into inexpressible transports of joy.

From that night the thoughts of the twain are filled with the perfections each sees in the other. Metham calls upon his divinity at her home, the coyness with which he is received fans the flame of his desire, he presses his suit and is dismissed with a most encouraging NO. He calls again. Then Mother intervenes and says it must all cease: this handsome young rake finds no favor in her eyes, in his ardor and good looks she reads only a menace to her daughter's peace of mind. Lord Tyrawley, too, frowns upon the attachment: she must have a husband—Mr. Crump, who is at hand "sighing like furnace." Coercion is hemming Anne into stark and deadly respectability. Easily led where her affections are engaged, they are genuinely given to her father and mother. Her evil star which she always claimed was in the ascendant at the crises of her life is particularly baleful.

Looking at Crump she finds him as unappetizing as his name.

Then there is Metham, who holds out—what?

Will she never know a genuine happiness? She is certain she prefers Mr. Metham to any man living, and she has no scruple in accepting his presents. There are stolen visits to his lodgings where Anne declares their conduct was most circumspect as "he never attempted even to salute me."

The night arrives when THE PROVOKED WIFE is performed with Quin in his admired part of *Sir John Brute* and Anne as *Lady Fanciful.* The amorous Crump sits beaming on the front row of the pit, drinking in those perfections that he is sure will soon be his, for have not his Lordship and Mrs. Bellamy gone so far as to draw up a marriage pact? All the spite and disdain that the author has given to the part of *Lady Fanciful* are rendered with rare spirit by Anne and hurled directly into the face of the adoring swain, too blind to think the shafts of anger are other than fine acting. The more spiteful *Lady Fanciful* becomes the more boisterous his plaudits and the louder his "bravas!" Anne froths with fury.

Metham stands behind the scenes the picture of woe, his good English complexion pallid, his features haggard. On her way from her dressing-room to the stage for the last act he accosts her and beseeches a word.

"Let it be quick," says Anne, "the curtain is about to go up."

"Not here then, for this may be the last time we shall ever speak together. Oh, I beg of you!"

They go hurriedly into the hallway leading to the stage door. Instantly she is caught up by the bold Lochinvar and with all her stage frippery rushed through the passage, out at the door and thrust into a waiting coach.

Inside Covent Garden there is confusion and amazement. The audience is jeering and clamoring over a delayed curtain. The stage manager has his finger on the signal for commencement. Where is Bellamy? A call boy is running from room to room, shouting, "Lady Fanciful! Lady Fanciful!" There is no reply. *Lady Fanciful* is on her way to liberty and love.

For many a day London saw nothing of the beautiful Bellamy—she was living in a fool's Paradise, hoping that some day her lover will make her Lady Metham. From their honeymoon nest out in Lieces-terfields where rapture and forgetfulness hold sway they draw farther and farther afield from the town where the episode at Covent Garden is more than a seven days' wonder, kept alive by paragraphs in the public prints and Peg Woffington's tongue, until they reach the city of York, and here her baby is born.

Says Anne, "The eleventh day of my illness my ever-regretted George Metham first saw the light, and I may truly say blest me in making me the mother of a man child. Had death spared him he would now, I doubt not, have made my old age comfortable."

The news reaches Mrs. Bellamy—she flies to York, her outraged propriety forgotten, nurses her little grandson and never gives Metham a moment's peace until he promises to make her daughter his wife. It was easy to promise what he had no idea of making good. The Elysium so golden several months ago was losing its luster. The household budget was running low; Anne's funds and those of her mother were swept away; Metham, whose family was scandalized by this runaway match, made matters worse by plunging into disastrous ventures at the gaming table. Lord Tyrawley helped out the situation, but with some resentment, and old friends in London were not unsympathetic, but all was not enough—Anne must have money—and York was no place in which to procure it. Back then to London to gay living, outspoken admirers and lavish purses. Leaving her baby in care of his grandmother, she found herself once more in the life she loved, engaged this time by the parsimonious Garrick at a none-too-liberal salary for Drury Lane Theatre. Old friends renew their cordial relations, the minister, Fox, whose name had been continually linked with hers, gives substantial proof of his welcome, her house becomes a salon for the fast set. There is no lack for money—occasionally she finds packets of bank-notes on the mantel of her drawing-room or reposing blissfully in flower vases.

General Wall and the Comte Haslang in conjunction with the Marquis de Vernueil propose that she set up what she terms a "Pharaoh bank" (it has a familiar sound), and Anne borrows money and pawns her diamonds. Notwithstanding overflowing patronage and high play the scheme fails, and Anne is obliged to discharge her cook. She must go to work again. Metham exhibits extraordinary complaisance the while; he has set up his own establishment elsewhere in London.

The season at Drury Lane opens with a revival of ROMEO AND JULIET with Garrick and Bellamy as the two lovers. Once more Anne feels the thrill of the acted scene and breathes the incense of adulation from the crowded houses who again pay their tribute of tears to the woes of *Juliet*. Perhaps the heart agonies she had passed through had given to her a greater power of emotion, a more eloquent expression, more gentleness.

Over at Covent Garden Rich was not to be outdone: he, too, opened his theatre with ROMEO AND JULIET, with the lovely and tragic Mrs. Cibber as the heroine. The town was divided in its allegiance, not only between the two *Juliets* but the *Romeos* as well; Garrick had a serious opponent in the graceful and silver-tongued Spranger Barry.

Garrick, all fire and impetuosity, threw the audience into an expectancy that he would climb the balcony to the arms of his lady-love; and as for Barry, he inspired one matinée-idol worshiper of the day to exclaim, "Had I been *Juliet*, so tender, so eloquent and so seductive was he I should certainly have gone down to him."

By every *coup-de-théâtre* the opposing managers strove to outdo each other; Rich, an eighteenth century P. T. Barnum, advertised for his production a *grand funeral procession* with all the trappings of pageantry, mourners and banners, horses and donkeys in the pomp of sable and silver and a dirge-breathing band!

Courtesy of the Harvard College Library, Theatre Collection

Mr. Garrick and Mrs. Bellamy in the characters of *Romeo* and *Juliet*

In this rivalry old friendships were broken; each faction vaunted the supremacy of its idol—the Barryites decried the acting of Garrick and Garrick's friends pooh-poohed that of Barry, while in the coffee-houses the supporters of Bellamy and Cibber came to blows, and often swords were drawn. The feuilletonists made jingles about it.

A bit of doggerel that became popular was:

> "Well, what's tonight?" says angry Ned
> As from his bed he rouses.
> "Romeo again?" He shakes his head,
> "A plague on both your houses!"

Occasionally the managements substituted another play, but on these nights the houses had to be *papered* to secure an audience. Finally the warfare ceased.

The season prospered. Outside the theatre Anne's extravagances continued unabated, her debts accumulated but she gave them little thought—*somebody* must pay them.

Now and then Metham strolled upon the festive scene rather pleased than otherwise that the woman so easily won by him should be the center of such attraction—and *he* so little out of pocket thereby! In an unfortunate hour he brought along a friend, Calcraft. It was an occasion which Anne had especially designed as a complimentary supper to her lover. He had been negligent of late, preferring the doubtful joys of the gaming tables where now and then he made a winning, but more often lost heavily. She surveyed her feast with pride, it was worthy of her brilliant company and surely of the man she had of late urgently sought to make her his wife.

The newcomer, known as *Honest* Jack Calcraft, was courteous and respectful, but he was all eyes for his hostess: from the first glance he made up his mind that fealty to his friend, Metham, should mean nothing to him.

The lavishness of the entertainment was freely discussed by her guests.

"Egad!" whispered one, "who is to pay for all this?"

Anne caught the remark. With an intriguing smile and the prettiest blush in the world she said, "Oh, I'm not in fear of being detained for debt in the Rules of the Kings Bench because of it, but if that *should* be I hope some one of you will release me."

The master of the feast struggled unsteadily to his feet with bloodshot eye, heated with his wine.

"If that should be," he rasped, "you may rot there before *I* will release you."

In the dead pause that followed Calcraft rose and, with a bow to his hostess, said, "I hope, sir, you will not be angry with those that will."

It was not without a heartbreak that she gave up Sir George Metham; to her dying day the father of her son was the great love of her life. That it was not legalized by marriage she excused by saying, "In the eye of Heaven such a connection when conducted with this propriety may not need the repetition of the nuptial ceremony. Curse on all laws but those which love has made!"

The moil of debts and the tedious business of evading creditors with bailiffs' attachments left Anne but little ruffled. She shook off her embarrassments like dew from the petals of a rose. Her popularity grew. If by chance she found it waning she readily revived public interest by an outburst that would be sure to register—she specialized in sensation. Swept away with horror at the sight of *Laius'* ghost, while playing in Œdipus, she shrieked and fell and before the gaze of the amazed spectators was borne senseless from the scene.

A kingling from a neighboring court came with pomp and circumstance to England. Frequently the chafing occupation of sitting on the throne of Denmark irked him and he fled across the Channel for relieving visits to his brother-in-law, the young George III in London, and to behave abominably in public places. He was wont to exhibit his insolences of loud talking and jeering criticism in the royal box of the theatre to the great resentment of the players. If Anne could not go to France to captivate Louis XV, royalty came to her: he "commanded" a performance of Jane Shore and showed his appreciation of its beauties by sinking into a snoring slumber. Bellamy was playing the wronged *Alicia* who expends much blank verse energy in cursing her betrayer, *Hastings,* and was fuming with humiliation at the ill manners of the sovereign. Presently the King roused from his happy dreams, his somnolent eye fell upon the figure of a bedizened lady facing the box in the glow of the smoking foot-lamps and apparently addressing him.

"O, thou false lord!"—she thundered,
"Hither you fly and here you seek repose:
Spite of your poor deceit your arts are known.
Dost thou in scorn
Preach patience to my rage and bid me tamely
Sit like a poor contented idiot down
Nor dare to think thou'st wronged me? Ruin seize thee,
And swift perdition overtake thy treachery!"

Never had the lines of Nicholas Rowe's tragedy been given with such poignant novelty. The audience rocked with ecstasy, and amid the laughter the amazed King spluttered: "The baggage! the impudent baggage! Gad! I'd not be married to a woman with such a voice though she brought me the whole world for a dowry."

It required a little time for Anne to become used to Calcraft; she found it difficult to accept *Benvolio's* advice,

"Take thou some new infection to thy eye,
And the rank poison of the old will die."

Although she acknowledged his good points of complexion, eyes and auburn hair, his manly, handsome face and well-made person she found he had a slouch, contracted, possibly, from his *not having learned to dance,* an embonpoint and "certain vulgarity in his figure which was *rather disgusting.*"

This inability to measure up to Anne's standard of perfection was not of permanence, worthy qualities of mind and heart which the generous Anne mistakenly read into his character perhaps balanced the scales. No doubt an added piece of gallantry of her new lover had something to do with it. While she was standing in the wings that were crowded with the town dandies, ready to go on the stage for her part, she was rudely accosted by a person in liquor; Calcraft, who was standing by like a melodrama hero, knocked him down and when he was able to rise invited the disturber to go outside with him. The following day Calcraft appeared at Anne's lodgings with the culprit in hand and forced him to apologize. This he did awkwardly, muttering something about actresses having so little sense of delicacy that they might be accosted with impunity. Metham, striving to be reinstated in favor, was present and, to the astonishment of every one, solemnly declared, "Sir, that lady is to be my wife!"

Ignoring all handicaps we find the lady, under the guidance of a shrewd old friend, making a thoroughly businesslike contract with Calcraft. She was not always dramatizing her emotions and swooning away in crises. Calcraft was willing to agree to anything except the immediate ceremony of marriage—he was not in position, he said, to support a household establishment. However he expected an ample allowance would be made him at the end of six years, and put his signature to an agreement that on or before the termination of this period the marriage should be solemnized under forfeiture of forty thousand pounds.

The knowledge of this contract inflamed Metham beyond words: he forced himself, seemingly insane, into Anne's presence, and with drawn sword declared that unless she returned to him they should die together. The little boy, who was playing in the room, shrieked in terror, crying, "Oh, mama! my mama!" Bellamy adroitly fainted and the episode ended.

It was thus that the new compact was entered upon, an arrangement not destined for unalloyed happiness. Viewing the affair in her later years Anne moralized. "We vainly flatter ourselves with tasting unembittered pleasures. To every condition are annexed its advantages and disadvantages. Even a monarch sleeping under canopies of costly state and lulled with sounds of sweetest melody can sometimes envy the peaceful slumbers of the meanest wretch."

In a little box called Ragman's Castle near Twickenham the twain passed a pleasant summer, Anne lashing herself into the belief that she was content but really succeeding quite badly, though Calcraft was desperately in love. Financial matters were not what they should have been, it required the utmost of their joint income to meet demands, notwithstanding that the occasional appearance of mysterious bank-notes from *unknown friends* allowed Anne to pay all her debts. She, at least, met the situation squarely. But the truth is she never was completely happy away from the theatre.

Here her attraction remained unabated; her benefit at the conclusion of the season was a huge affair. She chose VENICE PRESERVED for the event; the Earl of Mansfield was present and was fascinated with her acting, saying, "I came to admire Garrick but go away enchanted with Bellamy," a speech that was not wholly approved by the envious Garrick.

In due time the arrival of a little daughter put an end for a long time to Anne's appearances before her public.

In the interim things did not run smoothly in the Calcraft-Bellamy ménage—clouds of discontent began to gather as they were sure to do over such an ill-advised union, even had it been a legitimatized one. It soon became evident that if money were to be forthcoming Anne would be compelled again to put herself into the gay life of the theatre and of the town, where the lure of her beauty and her accomplishments had cash value. She was learning that her helpmeet was something of a fraud, and in the face of all his pretentions a liar and a cad. His financial prospects grew constantly dimmer, it is doubtful if this *honest* Jack Calcraft ever possessed any real ones. He would have had none had she not exerted her influence in high circles and found him a government position; then with a semblance of cooperation they took an expensive London establishment with a small army of servants.

Anne found herself the guarantor for the major part of their obligations, but she gave the matter little thought: borrowing was not difficult, tradesmen were easily put off, the visits of Secretary Fox, who now held the portfolio of the Navy, were of a consoling character and there were still anonymous gifts of bank-notes to eke out her salary at the theatre.

There were gay parties, *petit soupers,* high play, everywhere was brilliancy, rare talk and exchange of wit except where Calcraft sat apart hugging his boorishness alone, quite unable to compete and out of it all. Like the seepage from a damp and unhealthy cellar wall his crass qualities oozed from him and dripped baneful, inescapable upon the disillusioned Anne.

She discovered she had never loved him; her attempts to polish him were ridiculous failures, his inept hide could not take the polish.

Through sheer boredom she decided to become a blue stocking and turned to science; there had been enough learned discussion at her house—why not become a *femme savante?* Here was a rôle she had never played—a female Newton! Finding herself unequal to it she attended lectures on astronomy and advanced so far as to be able, as she turned her azure eyes heavenward, to decipher the Ram, the Bull, the Lion and the Scorpion.

Having thus conquered the essential principles

of astronomy she looked for more worlds, and took up natural philosophy, but abandoned it when she saw a cat tortured by an air pump, "though it is an animal I have the greatest dislike to." Then, with dreams of becoming another Maintenon, she went in for politics. Within a week 'twas all forgotten. But that was Anne. She lashed herself into spasms of high resolve one moment and forgot them the next. And surely higher education need go no further; here was food sufficient for gossip at the supper table. In the field of politics her only recorded activity was in the cause of Fox over a contested election at Windsor, where the exercise of her blandishments got her into hot water with some rowdy voters.

There was a malign influence in her association with Henry Fox. This first Baron Holland had a bad record, politically and socially: he was an adept in the arts of dissipation to whose practises he early introduced his illustrious son, Charles James. When Charles was a mere lad his prodigal father carted him over the Continent, introducing him to all the immoral society of Europe.

Three times was Henry Fox made minister and as often unmade in twenty-four hours.

Into this desert of tedium came the advent of Dodsley's CLEONE, to which reference has been made, an eighteenth-century EAST LYNNE, built out of sob stuff. In the woes of the heroine Anne's lachrymal talents had complete sway and swept a full tide of fortune into the coffers of Manager Rich;

every tear meant a guinea in the box office. It became the fashion to go and weep with Bellamy.

She had been wise enough to see that the grandiose manner, so long in vogue, of portraying the woes of distressed heroines would be out of place in this piece and adopted a simple, colloquial method which had brought down the prophecy of complete failure from the onlookers at rehearsals.

She said, "The unaffected naïveté which I intended to adopt in the representation was accompanied by the same simplicity in my dress. This was perfectly *nouvelle,* as I had presumed to leave off that unwieldy part of a lady's habiliments called a hoop, a decoration which, at that period professed *nuns* appeared in, as well as with *powder in their hair.*"

Anne's most sanguine hopes were exceeded; even Doctor Johnson was heard to exclaim from his place in the pit, "I will write a copy of verses upon her myself."

I would that we might leave the Bellamy here on the pinnacle of her popularity! But it would be sheer inhumanity to do so. Our manifest duty is to lead her carefully and tenderly from the height where she stands elate with her arms a-stretch to all the joys of the world. For her mountaintop is a volcano threatening every moment to irrupt and engulf her in a fiery flood.

To follow her through her various adventures is like viewing THE PERILS OF PAULINE in the films; hair-breadth 'scapes, a rescue from the knife attack of a lunatic, entanglements in the law, the treachery of friends, robberies of her jewels by trusted servants, accidents, injuries, well-nigh fatal illnesses, an escape with valuable records from a burning building, investments in schemes that were merely swindling operations, evasion of visits by the bailiffs, threats of the debtor's prison, traductions of her character by the scandal sheets, ablaze with jewels one day and the next seeking relief from the pawnbrokers,—all these were but as trifles compared to the blow that fell at the discovery that Calcraft could never make good his contract of marriage because he already had a living wife. Murder came into her heart then, and would have been attempted had she not in her furious endeavor to reach him fallen into a paroxysm and subsequent insensibility.

Notwithstanding her estimate of Calcraft's character, that "he was cold even to cowardice, rapacious, insolent and mean to the lowest pitch of parsimony," she had ever been considerate toward the worthless fellow. She more than kept up her share of the family obligations, she was for ever finding excuses for his boorish manners, and when he was seized with an illness she became his devoted, unselfish nurse. Indeed her traits of generosity, sympathy and kindliness are altogether charming.

But the moment had come to write finis to the Calcraft phase of her life. He often came whining at her door to find it shut to him. Behind that barrier a scene was enacting that filled his soul with fury—a group of anxious people listening to the first cry of a little boy baby whom Baron Holland, in the greatness of pride and satisfaction over his paternity declared should be named Henry Fox!

The seasons came and went in gray monotony, bringing little of profit or happiness in the theatre. There were no new successes for her, but there were new faces and comely ones that were causing the hum of laudation from the habitués of Covent Garden. Anne's nights grew fewer. Something vital and necessary was seeping from her life—admiration. There were days when her adored London became hateful—when she sat alone and her servants were posted at her door to keep every visitor from entering—when she refused to be dressed or to be served with food, when she beat the pillows of her bed with wrath, while her clock ticked time's relentless march down the long lane from nights of triumph and days of delight.

She must get away—where? There was Ireland. Surely, in Dublin she was not forgotten. To think was to act, and to act was to give her back her light-heartedness. There was little difficulty, an engagement of rich promise was negotiated, and leaving every obligation of indebtedness, not the least of which was the forfeiture of two thousand pounds for the breaking of her London contract, to be settled in whatever way blind fate chose, we find her in her coach posting along the road to Holyhead without a care in the world. She may have left bankruptcy behind her, but my lady certainly traveled in state—two postillions, a guide, a footman and *three* maids.

The Bellamy that now presented herself at the Smock Alley Theatre was a far different being from the enchantress the tales of whose witchery had persisted in Dublin for thirteen years. The truth is she had lived too hard, too fast, the scars of a life of intense emotion and the tearing tooth of illness were showing, cruel as the ravages of the fields of Flanders, and Anne was losing her beauty.

The eager crowd that gathered to gaze at the famous siren on the arrival of her coach at her lodgings beheld "a little dirty creature, enfeebled by her journey, bent nearly double with fatigue, her countenance tinged with the jaundice, and in every respect the reverse of a person who could make the least pretentions to beauty;" they looked at one another, wondered and vanished, leaving her to "crawl into the house without molestation."

A few days' rest: the magic of transformation is accomplished and Anne comes upon the stage almost—but not quite—her old self as *Belvidera.* But the wild plaudits that had greeted her early appearances are absent, the potent charm that had swayed all Dublin has become a mere memory.

To one young man there is no flaw in her perfections, he burns his incense and bows his head in mute worship, he looks upon her with eyes of awe and prays to all the heathen gods and little fairies of Ireland to make her his own. This is the Apollo Belvidere of the Dublin stage, the *jeune premier par excellance,* the breaker of the hearts of Dublin ladies, he of the soulful eye and melancholy mien, the sighing swain of all the romantic plays in Smock Alley—one *Digges*—why have these eighteenth-century Adonises such unromantic names? That *she* should be sent by the Erse fairies to bless his vision—that he should breathe the same air with her, walk in her footsteps and in playing opposite her, clasp her in his very arms! She, the heroine of a hundred tales of gallantry, the enslaver of a thousand susceptible souls, the modern Circe, the Bellamy!

Anne has heard of his reputation, and keeps him at his distance. Coyly she withdraws her fingers from his fierce hot hands in their love scenes. She is formal, gracious and kindly, but cold as ice to his advances. Propitious fortune gives him opportunity of calling at her house with other visitors; standing in dumb and "awful respect" before her, Anne has time to appraise his points and finds that "as he was really the accomplished gentleman and an entertaining companion it was impossible to resist being pleased with his company."

Still the citadel remained proof against attack, the art of defense, which means the art of allure, was one that Anne had long been schooled in, until the lucky chance of a seizure of her body for a debt of two hundred pounds gave opportunity for the warlike Digges to pummel the offending Shylock to within an inch of his life, and then the besieged one capitulated, released the drawbridge chain, and handed over the keys with a smile. And why should she not warm her heart once more at the fire of romance? He was young, talented, and when she contrasted him with the ungainly actors of the troup who put her in mind of "Sir John Falstaff's ragged regiment, a part of which he had robbed the gibbets of" he was a star i' the darkest night.

This was the one bright moment of consolation in her rash Dublin venture; as far as Anne was concerned it was a deserted and sacrificed city.

To return were as tedious as to go o'er, but it must be accomplished. Could she but find her falconer's voice to lure this tassel-gentle, this London, back again all might yet be well. There was a moment of tawdry glory. Through the smoke and fog of London, always incense to her nostrils, crept an echo of old adulation. No one, even in this heartless, thoughtless town could wholly forget the Bellamy, and her nights at Covent Garden were still of value to Rich who readily entered upon a new contract with her. There were others besides her decimated troup of luke-warm lovers who could not and would not forget her—her creditors! Old scores had to be evened.

Her Apology now becomes a sordid and painful catalogue of cash transactions, and few, alas! on the credit side, lawsuits, attachments, loan offices, defalcations on the part of those she trusted, payments and non-payments, it is all money—*money.* And it is not that money meant anything to her; rather it is because it did not.

"Why am I persecuted by the hateful thing, and by what right do they take my diamonds and my pretty gowns from me? Isn't it enough for the milliner that she receives the honor of making robes for the Bellamy? How easy it had been to settle every troublesome affair had I been so minded! Among the competitors for my favor, which were numerous, there was one who offered me ten thousand pounds to be admitted as a favored lover. As the gentleman is now happily married I will not mention his name."

To avoid arrest for debt she planned to escape to Holland, but was prevented at Harwich by a contrary wind which made the sailing of the packet impossible for some days. She went into hiding in a neighboring village. Here Digges, who had been playing in Scotland, found her, and under pretense of effecting her safety, and though, her luggage being aboard the Harwich packet, she had no apparel with her but "a few shifts, my nightdress and the habit I had on," he carried her off to Edinburgh. This city was so detestable to her that, to avoid a public appearance there, "I took a pair of scissors and cut my hair off quite close to my head." When she was finally induced to appear she was compelled to repair the result of her vandalism with mountains of false hair. And pity 'tis the wilful bobbed-hair little devil should not have shown that charming shorn head to the public!

Two Scottish seasons with Digges were the outcome of this escapade and they were not wholly unhappy.

It matters little how often the London maelstrom whirls her to its outer rim it inescapably draws her back each time with a more powerful clutch of the vortex. For her thoughtless signature on a paper of seeming inconsequence she barely eludes Newgate prison and is saved by the timely arrival of friends who lift the obligation. She is compelled, however, to live within the Rules of the King's Bench in a little, vile lodging belonging to The Windmill in St. George's Fields for which wretched accommodation she is forced to pay two guineas a week. Here she is attended only by a small slattern who follows her mistress into exile with wails of distress, and rebels against being sent away. So curtailed is her wardrobe that when she is finally freed from durance she is obliged to borrow even an under petticoat.

She is soon back at Covent Garden acting and content, all-be-it she must take the buffet of fortune in the shape of parts of diminished importance.

But the few friends who are loyal, and those of her kin remaining to her, one by one are stricken by death and whatever legacies that might have reverted to her are lost in Anne's lack of foresight in legal formalities—Henry Woodward, the actor, who was devoted to her, Lady Tyrawley, then Tyrawley himself—her own father—and finally her mother.

Anne is growing embittered and hardened. Wherever she has looked for bread she has received a stone.

In the welter of her woes she made one pathetic

gesture of supremacy. Rich revived King Lear, the part of *Cordelia* being assigned to Anne. It was to be her first appearance after the settlement of her late financial embarrassments. The recollections of her tribulations melted into air in the eagerness of making ready for the part. When her study and costume were complete Rich changed his mind and announced a young, beautiful but inexperienced Miss Wilford for *Cordelia,* substituting her name for the Bellamy's on the bills. Anne had not forgotten the art of creating a sensation; she secretly had hand-bills printed setting forth her ill treatment and claiming her prior right in the character. These were handed by her servant to each patron as he entered the theatre. When young Miss Wilford made her entrance the house resounded with cries of "Off! Off! We want Bellamy." Anne, dressed and waiting, when the offender was removed, made her entree, as she says, "amidst an universal applause, and I do not recollect that I ever met with more tokens of approbation during my theatrical existence."

But, mingled with the shouts of approval she may have heard the mocking laughter of all the dead-and-gone *Cordelias* whose laurels had been torn from their own brows by younger, comelier hands.

Westminster Tower is marking the passage of time, sending its sixteen-note peal into the night to tell the wakeful citizens that it is about to strike two. The steeple of St. Martin's-in-the Fields has been caught napping and fails to broadcast its announcement until it is four full beats behind. Cityward St. Clement's Danes and Bow Church are joining the chorus; St. Sepulchre's on the Viaduct is sending its booming notes rolling across London Bridge to meet a tinkle from St. Mary Overy's in Southwark that has been so scandalously late in waking up it lags arear all the others, timid and apologetic. Each one holds stubbornly to its own notion of the correct pitch, but in the melting-pot of the dense fog discord is fused into higher harmony.

If you are an epicure in London fogs you realize that this one assaults the tongue with a more acrid taste than usual, there is something poisonous about it.

A night pedestrian, whom insomnia has routed from his bed, is making his way past the Parliament Houses; he is wrapped to the eyes in his greatcoat (it is penetrating, this March night), on whose shoulder-capes the moisture condenses into drops that gleam like moonstones as he passes under the feeble glare of Westminster Bridge lamps. He wipes the viscous glaze from his lips but it soon gathers anew.

Through the curtain of the fog comes the rumble of a heavy vehicle and the pounding of hoofs; now it bursts into sight tearing along like the Wild Huntsman and is swallowed up again, leaving behind a trail of howls, oaths and song catches—a drunken party Holborn-bound from Vauxhall. Over on the Surrey side of the river there is a far-off whir of a watchman's rattle and the muffled yells of "Stop thief!" echoing against warehouse walls. Then all is silent once more. The miasmic air seems thick with hidden presences—eyes that peer through the mist, ears that listen to one's breathing, and yet, for all he can hear or see, the man in the caped coat might be miles above the earth.

A dark speck in the luminous haze becomes by a species of theatrical legerdemain a shabby shivering harlot who lurches against the man with a cry of joy and hope. She presses her frail body into the folds of his greatcoat for very warmth and pours out a stream of pleadings. He is sympathetic—that is all. With a little wail that is half a laugh she blots herself out, going northward.

The man has drawn himself into a recess of the bridge just as a black robed figure pauses on the spot where he had been standing. She is lightly clad but seems not to be minding the cold. For several minutes she is motionless, then slowly she creeps down the slime-covered steps to the river's edge. On the lowest stone she lays aside her bonnet and apron and sits watching the Thames flood as it pours upward on its rise from the sea. There is a spot of brightness from a full moon seeping through the fog, by its vague light the woman sees the up-journeying flotsam and jetsam kotowing in the surface scum like a file of crazy Moslem worshipers.

The subdued and guarded click of oars—she shrinks back, her black dress melting into the mass of the wall. With stealthy stroke a river thief sneaks by; then, after an interval, the sharp man-o'-war boat of heavy sweeps and the river constable's barge shoots past, a man with a lanthorn in the bow peering to right and to left.

Now there is no life except at either end of the stone stairway—the man in the capes watching the silent figure below. He may have to effect a rescue down there presently. After all what business is it of his?—And yet—— The flood creeps up the granite blocks of the wall—soon it will reach the step. The woman's lips are moving, though the face is set and, but for a rigid stare, quite expressionless.

A Thames rat, evil and dripping, hoists himself from below by the lambrequin of slippery weeds, cocks an appraising eye at the silent woman, then skurries across the hem of her skirt, leaving a wet trail, and falls again with a *plop* into the tide. So intent is she upon her purpose she scarce rouses when an eddying bat brushes her cheek with its wing. Her foot slips over the step, she can just reach the ripples now. It is easier to let the river come to her than to throw herself in.

But another sound is mingling with the upward lapping of the water—some one is passing above: a tiny urchin who puts his head against the stone coping and sobs with hunger, and a gaunt mother who says she has nothing to give him, adding, "God's almighty will be done!"

The black figure below rouses and with a cry

makes its way up the stair. Here is misery greater than hers, and there are some stray half pence still left in her pocket.

Night was paling into the sallow mists of a London dawn when the man in the greatcoat delivered the terrified, trembling little woman, whose saturated black garments were streaked with green river slime, at her mean lodging, never knowing that the poor soul who had come so close to self-destruction was George Anne Bellamy.

Fortune has a tricksy way of throwing dust into our eyes and even after her dark hour Anne's world blazed with false hope. Bright days began again, she found she could still laugh, still love. But there was a spectre that knew the road to her bed of uneasy dreams—a spectre that grinned and jingled a bag of gold coins, and beyond it were reverberations of clanging iron doors and the clicking of prison locks.

On the stage of Covent Garden Theatre in 1784 waiting for the curtain to rise on a benefit performance in which a number of London's celebrated players are to appear, a wretched remnant of what was once the elfin Bellamy, broken, helpless through racking disease and old before her time, lies propped in a padded armchair. She is clad in faded tawdry garments that in the days of her glory served as models for the *beau monde* to copy. The wan features are raddled with rouge that only contrives to render more pitiless the inroads that have been made on their once perfect beauty. Her hands are clutching the arms of her chair, and her eyes are gleaming with unnatural brightness.

"Now get you to my lady's chamber and tell her, let her paint an inch thick to this favour she must come. Make her laugh at that."

Miss Farren, in front of the curtain, is speaking a rhymed farewell address. As she comes to the lines:

"But see, oppressed with gratitude and tears,
To pay her duteous tribute she appears"

the curtain rises, revealing the famous Bellamy. The entire house rises with it—old lovers and a young generation that has heard the legends of the Circe who filled an entire zoological garden with her conquests, coffee-house notables, curious idlers, cynics, even her enemies pay her a standing tribute. A wave of plaudits a flutter of fans and handkerchiefs—then a silence.

The bedizened little creature gazes bewildered at the multitude before her, but makes no response until, urged by Miss Farren, she bends forward from the cushions of her chair and murmurs a few words so feeble and indistinct they scarce can be heard. Then, with her clawlike hand waving an adieu and her sunken lips contorted into a smile, she sinks back and sees the curtain fall for the last time between herself and the public whose plaything she has been through years packed with more tumult than has fallen to the lot of even the most riotous of her sister sirens of the stage.

That this daughter of pleasure retained the friendship and sympathy of a few fine old comrades to the very last speaks well for her heart. She kept as brave a front as she might before them. You need only glance through her memoirs, which she wrote even while waiting the crash on her door that announced the bailiff who would again thrust her behind the walls of a debtor's prison, to find a childlike love for the beautiful things of life and a trust in human nature. That was her fatal weakness—she trusted it too far.

And yet had she to live her life again she would not have chosen the sterner path. She was a very gourmet of sensation and emotion. Only at rare moments did she view with envy the placid ones of the world.

"I am sometimes on the point of crying out, 'Happy people who pass through life in a state of enviable tranquillity! If ye do not taste the pleasures this sublunary state affords, neither do the pains with which it abounds pungently affect you.'" For all its punishments she would not exchange her susceptibility for the calm pleasures of unfeeling stoicism. "Give me my susceptibility," cries the incurably sentimental one, "though it be attended with more than proportionate unhappiness! The pleasures flowing from love and from philanthropy, neither of which can find a residence in a stoic's bosom, fully compensate for the augmented pains."

Her indomitable naïveté will not die: she reaped its rewards. Upon her memory De Maupassant might have pinned his mocking beatitude, "Blessed are the naïve for they shall see nothing but God!"

Her final release from trouble came toward the morning of a dismal February night of 1788,—then the London dawn, gray—misty—hopeless. There are few who know where she is buried.

If we believe what Anne tells us she was fifty-five, but there are those who say she was sixty-one. We must forgive her the lie of six years.

Gossiping and garrulous Tate Wilkinson, who never had any illusions about anybody wrote: "And Bellamy who once lolled in her chair and rolled in her chariot and all the vanities of the world ended her days in prison! I hope she is happy, as she endeavored to promote the comforts of others and never employed either riches or talents, when in affluence and splendor, to render any one miserable."

A not unworthy epitaph.

V

AN EIGHTEENTH-CENTURY BARNSTORMER

V

AN EIGHTEENTH-CENTURY BARNSTORMER

There were sounds of grief in Newgate Prison. The Reverend John Wilkinson had been judged guilty of an affront to the majesty of England's law, he had been in too great haste to join couples in holy wedlock in order that the ceremonial fee might bring relief to his pressing debts. Justice decreed that he be transported to America to atone for his misdemeanor through fourteen years of bitter exile, and the ship waited.

It had been two years since the Marriage Act of 1754 had been sent through Parliament. By its provision any clergyman performing a marriage without first publishing the banns or by a shorter route through Doctor's Commons should be branded as a felon, loathsome in the sight of a virtuous British public.

The Reverend John had deemed himself exempt from the restrictions of the Act, for he was His Majesty George III's chaplain of the Savoy, rector of Coyty in Glamorganshire, stipendiary curate of Wise in Kent and had been chaplain to Frederick, the late Prince of Wales. Royalty, however, is notoriously unremembering, even memories of spiritual solaces became dim. The humble petitions to "The King's Most Excellent Majesty" went unanswered and John Wilkinson stood within the clammy confines of Newgate saying good-by to his sobbing wife and his seventeen-year-old son, Tate. But even hearts of English oak may crack; before the convict ship was clear of the Channel the chaplain's troubles were over and when a storm drove the vessel into Plymouth Harbor his body was carried ashore and secretly buried.

It was this catastrophe that caused Tate Wilkinson to become a vagabond and a barnstormer. He might have become such in any case; he was one of those pests to the visitor in the household—a "smart" child given to showing off in the family drawing-room. A favorite imitation was one of his father. Clad in his sire's surplice and standing within the framework of a chair from which the cushion had been removed he provoked the rapture of his parents and the bored plaudits of the guests.

The family was left destitute—even the effects which the unfortunate John Wilkinson took aboard ship were not returned and there was little of their own between them and starvation. Influential friends there were, two of whom offered to procure Tate a commission in the army, but the pestiferous boy had dreams of his own; he wanted to be an actor. He had been to the theatre in London and had seen plays performed by Woffington, Mrs. Cibber, Garrick and Old Quin. He had given screaming imitations of these great people to an assembly of his cronies in Harrow School, at which he had become a most unwilling pupil, and he knew he could play

Romeo quite as well as Barry and equal Garrick as *Richard*.

Now nothing should deter him. He went secretly to Covent Garden where Manager Rich gave him a test, later some few hints of instruction, allowed him the privilege of freedom behind the scenes and after a few weeks, greatly to his astonishment, told him he wouldn't do at all for Covent Garden or any other theatre.

The mystery of this erratic treatment was solved when he beheld the baleful eyes of Peg Woffington fixed upon him and her denunciatory finger impaling his effrontery. He had indulged in his extraordinary but fatal talent for mimicry and had dared to give imitations of the lively Peg in the greenroom. Worse still he had been invited to sit in a friend's box where Mrs. Woffington was sure he was engaged in stealing her thunder.

"Merit you have none," she burst out, "charity you deserve not, for if you did my purse should give you a dinner. Your impudence to me last night where you had with such assurance placed yourself is one proof of your ignorance. Added to that I heard you echo my voice when I was acting, and I sincerely hope in whatever barn you are suffered as an unworthy stroller that you will fully experience the same contempt you dared last night offer me."

Tate declared that elsewhere was a world in which he could swear unforgiveness to his foes even in the grave, "where nothing—no nothing—can touch me further."

To his one friend in the company, Ned Shuter, he cried, "O God! what shall I do for bread? I had better exhibit in a barn, but am not sure I can get even that situation."

Fat Ned was sympathetic. He, too, had known contumely. He had begun life as a billiard marker and was so unlettered as to be scarce able to read the words of his rôles.

"Don't ye fret, young 'un. My benefit's not many nights away. I'll get up the farce of LETHE, I'll do *Lord Chalkstone* and you shall play Woodward's part, *The Fine Gentleman.* You'll be right as a trivet; parts make the actor, me boy, not the actor the parts." Shuter was as good as his word. He was a tremendous favorite and his benefit house was packed in front and overflowed to an amphitheatre built upon the stage itself. Into the midst of this throng strutted Tate the Bold, clad in an absurd costume all velvets and spangles, his hair in curl papers for the part of a finicky, accomplished man of the world. A shriek of derision greeted his appearance, but Shuter's friends good-naturedly countered with applause which rang throughout the entire performance. Tate swallowed the bait, hook and sinker, and believing himself a new-born Garrick took a sedan-chair when all was over, and had himself conveyed to his mother's lodgings that she and her friends might be dazzled by his idiotic attire.

A month later another beneficiary in the company included LETHE in his bill and Tate emerged again as *The Fine Gentleman,* this time more shabbily clad (he could not afford hire for his former splendor), but still gorgeous, and was driven from the stage with peals of mirth and universal hisses. Flight from London was now his only refuge. Whenever he ventured abroad from his mother's lodgings mocking grins met him at every street turn. He could not bear it. Fortunately a chance in a little scratch company at Maidstone presented, and thither he went fortified with five guineas that Mrs. Wilkinson had managed to scrape together, one black suit of clothes and two small bags. Here he strutted and bellowed as *Romeo, Orestes* and kindred characters but, alack the day! few of the townsfolk came to see him. His little store of guineas dwindled as he beheld the infinite poverty and uneasiness among his fellows. On his benefit night his net profit was one shilling sixpence and two pieces of candle!

Autumn found Tate a member of Garrick's noble organization at Drury Lane Theatre in London, but far from the seats of the mighty—he was but little more than a supernumerary at a salary of fifteen shillings a week.

During the winter he was lent to Foote and traveled with him from London for an engagement in Dublin, Garrick having told Foote that he was clever at imitations.

Samuel Foote was enormously popular in London and the provinces; in Dublin he was especially liked. A man of infinite comic ability, he was almost more an entertainer than actor, specializing in interludes, imitations and farces. His imitations of celebrated actors were quite irresistible to his admirers. David Garrick hated him while for pecuniary reasons he harbored him in his own company, valuing too well the guineas Foote's performances brought to the treasury of Drury Lane. But he writhed under the imitations that Foote gave of his *Romeo,* his *Lear* and his *Abel Drugger.* It was with a sigh of relief that David saw the satirical comedian depart for Ireland and in his company another imitator, Tate Wilkinson.

The night of Tate's appearance was announced, the bill stating:

AFTER THE PLAY
MR. FOOTE will give TEA.
Mr. Puzzle (the Instructor) MR. FOOTE.
First Pupil—by a Young Gentleman
(who never appeared on any stage before)

The occasion passed off with éclat. Foote's pupil pleased the genial Dublinites, his imitations were received with roars of approval. It was perhaps not with the most joyous appreciation that Foote listened to the music of the applause, particularly when the emboldened Tate suddenly conceived the idea of imitating *him.* Between the pair a frosty wall rose that never thawed from that night. As Garrick had squirmed under Foote's mimicry so Foote now shivered under Wilkinson's. The audience's cries of "Foote outdone!" were poison to his ear, but he had to listen to them yet again for TEA was served many nights in succession. To the close of this short Irish season Tate prospered, fell heir to some good parts, had a most remunerative benefit and departed for London with one hundred and thirty pounds in his pocket, clad like a courtier in silken hose and a fine new suit trimmed with gold lace.

He naturally looked for a renewal of his engagement at Drury Lane. Thinking to impress Garrick he presented himself before that august dictator in all the glory of his raiment surmounted by a gilt-trimmed "Kevenhuller" hat. I have searched through records and fashion plates that I might identify this particular head piece. I can not find it, but I am sure it must have been a creation of rare refulgence and worn with an air by Master Wilkinson (or as the Partingtonian manager, Rich, addressed him, Muster Williumskin). "Roscius," however, viewed these gauds with a fishy eye and told the egregious youth that a little accidental success in Dublin had turned his head; 'twas supreme effrontery in him to ask for reengagement and negotiations were at an end.

Wilkinson's portrait of the man who commonly stands for all that is accomplished and fine in the annals of the British stage, and whose name sheds glory upon his age, David Garrick, is curious and certainly unflattering. We know from other sources that David was notoriously penurious, but Wilkinson has no restraint whatever in his arraignment.

"Now Garrick was always on a fidget eager for attention and adulation, and when he thought himself free and adored would prattle such stuff as would disgrace a child of eight years old in conversation with its doting grandmama. His hesitation and never giving a direct answer arose from two causes—affectation and a fear of being led into promises he never meant to perform. Hence his halting: 'By—nay—— I—I cannot say but I *may* settle that matter and I—as I shall see you on Tuesday, why then—hey? You know that—— But Mrs. Garrick is waiting, and—I say now—hey? Tuesday—you will know, remember Tuesday?' As to money he seldom when walking the streets had any, therefore could not only lament his inability to give to a distressed suppliant; 'Why Holland,' or any other person who was with him, 'cannot you now advance half-a-crown, and be damned to you?' which if Holland did was a very good joke, and for fear of spoiling the jest he never paid Holland again. As to his vulgar vein of humor I confess I think it too gross to mention."

We can take this broadside with whatever grain of salt we may. It is inscribed in his Memoirs published twenty-one years after Garrick's death when there was little fear of a suit for libel. And for the greater part of Wilkinson's public career he was Garrick's mortal enemy.

Garrick had many enemies. In view of Davy's open dislike for Master Wilkinson it is somewhat surprising to find the *enfant terrible* a member of the Drury Lane Company at the opening of the season at a salary double his former one.

To Woffington, Tate's presence in the company was abhorrent.

Courtesy of the Harvard College Library, Theatre Collection

Tate Wilkinson

"By the living God!" exclaimed the outraged Queen, "I am amazed the fellow was not stoned in Dublin for his vile imitation of me."

Her protector, Colonel Cæsar, called on Garrick and informed him that if any imitation of his mistress were permitted on his stage he would call him out to render satisfaction for the insult.

Foote and his "pupil" appeared in a piece called THE DIVERSIONS OF THE MORNING. Wilkinson's début was favorably received, his clever imitations applauded, and there was no mimicry of Peg Woffington. David and the fiery Cæsar did not meet on the field of honor.

But the impudent upstart could not be suppressed; in subsequent representations of the skit that had brought him before the public he mimicked to the life all the favorites of both the patent houses and brought a storm of reprisal threats about his foolish young head—he did not stop for friend or foe—Foote, Shuter, Mrs. Clive, Barry, the mighty Roscius himself.

One night he found himself within a ring of protesting actors. "I stood," he says, "like a puppy dog in a dancing school when Mr. Mossop, the turkey-cock of the stage, with slow and haughty steps, all erect, his gills all swelling, eyes disdainful, hand upon his sword, almost bursting like the turkey with pride and hauteur and breathing as if his respiration was honour, began, 'Mr. Wilkinson! phew! (as breathing grand) *Sir,* Mister *Wil-kin-son! Sir!* I say—phew! how dare you make free in a public theatre with your superiors? If you were to take such liberty with me, *Sir,* I would draw my sword and run it through your body, *Sir!* You should not live, *Sir!'* and with the greatest pomp and grandeur made his departure."

Tate was with difficulty subdued, he became a favorite with his audiences, too profitable for the frugal Garrick to discharge and an implacable foe to his erstwhile mentor, the popular Sam Foote. When summer came he was barnstorming with inferior companies in the provinces, Portsmouth, Hull and elsewhere, mouthing as *Hamlet, Othello, Lear;* thinking enormously well of himself and convincing his hearers into the bargain.

Tate's chief asset, however, was his uncanny genius for mimicry. Actors were few in number in Garrick's day, fine ones rarer still, and these became so exalted in the public eye that when their gait, voice, accent were reproduced to rapturous applause, Wilkinson's vanity was flattered into regarding himself an artist of the highest rank. Not only did he satirize his fellow-players, but his craft brought before his audience the very persons of the non-conformist preachers, Whitfield and John Wesley, causing shrieks of delight to rise as with Whitfield's thunderous voice he shouted: "When you see the players on the stage you see the devil's children grinning at you, and when you go to the playhouse I suppose you go in ruffles. Did St. Paul wear ruffles? No! There were no ruffles in those days. I'm told the people say I bawl. I will not speak the word of *Gud* in a sleepy-manner like your velvet-mouthed preachers. *I will bawl!*"

Wilkinson's town engagements grew fewer. His admirers were discovering that imitation of the great ones, however perfect, was not greatness. The provinces called him. Ere he shook the dust of Drury Lane from his feet he knew the sweets of revenge long deferred. It concerned the piteous ending to the career of his nemesis, Peg Woffington.

She had romped through the joyous measures of As You Like It that night nearly to its close and had stepped forward to deliver *Rosalind's* epilogue to the audience. She reached the lines: "If I were a woman I would kiss as many of you as had beards that pleased me"—when paralysis seized her. She partly collapsed, staggered to the wings, and was carried, half fainting, to her dressing-room by young Tate Wilkinson. Through her bedridden years, the magnetic voice that had charmed thousands was heard with difficulty, but I am certain that at some time it spoke words of reconciliation and forgiveness for the youth who had caused her moments of distress. He had admired her greatly.

With a company of cheap actors, himself at their head, he could croak as the big frog in the little puddles of the lesser cities and think himself a king.

Nevertheless, he found himself a king who was compelled to bow to his subjects—the public. He relates:

"It was a horrid custom in these places for the performers, whether man or woman, to attend the play-bill man around the town, knock humbly at every door, supinely and obediently stop at every shop and stall and request the favor of Mr. and Mrs. Goodbody's company for his benefit at the theatre. Were she the heroine of the play she was (if married) equally responsible for steering *her* steps; be she *Juliet, Cleopatra,* or *Queen Elizabeth,* no dignity of any kind allowed for a violation of this duty, but incurred censure for pride, insolence and want of reverence. No matter how severe the weather, if frost, snow, rain or hail, *Jane Shore* and the proud *Lady Macbeth* were expected to pay equal deference. Only in the event of Lady Turtledove's being blessed with a loving mate was her attendance dispensed with, otherwise on no pretext whatever: the honour then devolved on the husband."

Another custom was to return thanks to the audience after the play; if the performers were married, both husband and wife must appear and avow their homage. Sometimes a group of off-spring, dressed in their best frocks, would troop on with their parents, smirking and courtseying their gratitude for the bounty of the self-satisfied spectators.

In the Lincolnshire town of Grantham the players were not only compelled personally to attend the distribution of hand-bills but to do so with the accompaniment of drum and trumpet, or else no attention would be paid to them. One day the ladies struck, they flatly refused to beg favors to the accompaniment of martial music. Hearing this the august Marquis of Granby, residing at Grantham, summoned the manager to his presence.

"Mr. Manager," said he, "I like a play. I like a player and shall be glad to serve you, but why are you all so suddenly offended at the noble sound of the drum? I like it and all the inhabitants like it. Put my name on the play bill as patron provided you drum but not otherwise."

There was no escape. *Mary, Queen of Scots, Henry the Eighth, The King of France,* and *Cardinal Wolsey* marched with the bill-passers, and drums rolled out the glory of the deed.

To all these practises Tate set a resolute face. He would not eat the bread of sycophancy, he would let his soul rot before he would be humiliated before all the marquises in the kingdom, and be damned to them!

It is not recorded that he said this to the noble Granby, but he stuck to his resolution and other managers tremblingly followed the example of Tate Wilkinson, first among theatrical rebels. "Good God!" he exclaims in his Memoirs, "what a sight to behold Mr. Frodsham, bred as a gentleman, with fine natural talents, and esteemed in York as a Garrick, running after or stopping a gentleman on horseback to deliver his benefit bill and beg half a crown as the price of a box."

On the lonely road that runs northward between Lincoln Edge and Lincoln Wolds a tiny cavalcade takes its way—some are afoot, some perch in a baggage wagon atop a heap of royal regalia, thrones, crowns and truncheons. Spears, guns and halberds bristle dangerously from the sides of the cart; on either side of the driver's seat the Lion of England and the Lilies of France wave in the breeze that wafts over the moorland. In shabby greatcoats, patched boots, torn gloves, their jowls blue with much shaving, long scraggly locks escaping beneath hats trimmed with tarnished gold lace and worn jauntily askew, march the men with triumph in their mien. The melancholy tragedian stalks with an abstracted air, glimpsing afar theatres filled with awe-struck spectators thrilling to the eloquence of his *Cato* and his *Brutus*. The fat comedian at his right, striving with ineffectual short legs to keep his stride, spouts a mocking imitation of the tragic one's declamation to the infinite delight of the "old man," the "heavy man" and the "utility" corps.

The ladies perched on the wardrobe boxes and the property crates containing the trumpets of RICHARD III, the pickaxes and spades, coffin and skulls of HAMLET and the thunder and lightning of MACBETH, gossip vigorously, mend torn chemises and preen their tattered finery. In a little rickety gig drawn by a limping horse at the head of the procession, rides the impresario whom the enraged Foote of Drury Lane had called a "pug-nosed s—— of a b——," the leading lady by his side, and on a scantling fixed between the shafts of the vehicle sits a man with a drum rolling defiance to all the tyrants of the world, crying liberty of the Magna Charta and the proclamation that under no circumstances of coercion will Britons ever, *ever* be slaves, especially to the lords of Lincolnshire.

Thus traveling they come out of the land of Egypt, cross the Humber and arrive at the city of Hull in the pleasant province of York.

The Wilkinson fortunes prospered, his purse fattened. He accumulated reputation and patronage in the towns of North Briton. His clowning and his imitations of noted actors of London were sources of joy to the provincials although the points of the latter were often missed by those who had no knowledge whatever of the great originals, Garrick, Foote, Barry, Mrs. Clive, Peg Woffington, Kemble, Cooke and Mrs. Siddons. Soon he was able to abandon the cart of Thespis, his shabby fit-up productions and his tattered army of strollers.

He obtained letters patent giving him the control of theatres in the important places. He refurbished his scenery and his paraphernalia, scrubbed up the shabby old playhouses and improved the personnel of the company. Not always was he successful in sustaining the gesture of disdain he directed at the arbiters of the vagabond players in Lincolnshire. Servility to the great he might deplore but to live he must practise it. The theatre was a fragile plant only thriving when watered by the patronage of the fashionable world.

The years of success and good-living were mellowing him, and he took to his growing popularity with graciousness. Garrick and Cooke, Kemble and the august Sarah Siddons might shake the theatrical world of London with their mellow thunder, but he, Tate Wilkinson, was King of the North. "The Wandering Patentee" of York, Manchester, Newcastle-on-Tyne, Hull, Wakefield, Leeds, Doncaster and Pontefract, with perpetual grants for the monopoly of their theatres. And when the comfort of later years lured him from the irksome and uncertain labor of acting and management he took up his pen to make little pictures of the noble figures of the stage, acknowledging their genius but finding their shams. Garrick he never could see otherwise than as a sawdust-stuffed doll, but he was forced to admit his success.

Great favorites of the London stage rose to pinnacles of popular favor and then dipped to the dregs of destitution. Garrick, to be sure, prospered and retired with a fortune. Of Peg Woffington his memory brings the picture of her last night at Drury Lane when paralysis stopped her tongue.

The beautiful Bellamy seducing all London with her charms and grinning in ghastly travesty of beauty at the end.

Mrs. Robinson ("Poor Perdita") whom George IV wooed, won and then tossed aside to heartbreak and poverty.

Dora Jordan, mothering a squadron of Hanoverian offspring by the Duke of Clarence and laughing herself into obscurity.

The celebrated Lucy Cooper once the sensation of London's social set, writing piteously to Wilkinson from a debtor's prison.

And Mossop! Mossop the turkey cock who had threatened the young Tate with his sword for daring to imitate his superiors! He falls like Woolsey with his greatness a-ripening and Tate sees him "perishing for want at Chelsea without common necessities, food or clothing and carried to his place of rest without leaving the means of payment for his burial rites."

The Wandering Patentee lingered in his retirement until 1805, somewhat broken in health and rather straitened in circumstances. He had saved little from his abundantly profitable ventures, but he had not lost his keen wit and his penetrating observation of the foibles of his fellows of the theatre. The varying tides of his fortunes, now rising to affluence and then ebbing almost to bankruptcy had been destined to hand his name to posterity. On their streams float many rich episodes of the country theatres, and anecdotes of the temperamental strollers of his day, caught in the net of his whimsical scrutiny and given to us in his MEMOIRS and in his WANDERING PATENTEE.

These folk lived in their own little world of the stage, set apart by the ancient edict that actors came legally under the class of "rogues and vagabonds." Their mimic lives were far more real to them than their dreary existence in cheap lodgings, to-day feeding on crusts and to-morrow feasting like lords at the ale-house. The language of royal courts became their daily speech, they addressed each other in the manner of kings and queens, quoting remembered lines from oft-repeated plays. The film of fantasy blinded their eyes to the actual world. Their eyes were always turned London way, their slumbers filled with dreams of the day when their names should shine in golden letters there—dreams that would never know fulfillment. They were all gently, deliciously mad.

"Ah me!" says Tate, "the actor's fame, however great, can not be recollected many years beyond the time he lived, for as Garrick observed:

> " 'But he who struts his hour upon the stage
> Can scarce extend his fame for half an age;
> No pen nor pencil can the actor save,
> The art and artist share one common grave.' "

VI

THE DELECTABLE DORA JORDAN

VI

THE DELECTABLE DORA JORDAN

WHEN this lively little lady emerged from the provincial theatres of Great Britain to storm the citadel of London in 1785 and carry all before her at Drury Lane as *Peggy* in THE COUNTRY GIRL she was a far more assured actress than the fragile, trembling girl that three years before had implored the patentee of the Leeds theatre, Tate Wilkinson, to give her just one chance.

To her pleadings had been added those of her mother and, unable to withstand the importunings of the suppliants, Wilkinson had yielded with what grace he could and no little misgiving. On the night of her appearance she found herself surrounded by foes in the company. The women had sensed a dangerous rival to their supremacy and had joined in a determined effort to blast every hope of success she could aspire to. They would show the young upstart!

There had been agonizing rehearsals with actors standing in the shadow of the wings tittering and jeering at her efforts. The conspiracy had been carried on with great secrecy under Wilkinson's nose. She had seen but too clearly the resentment that everywhere confronted her, but she dared not raise her voice. Costumed for the part of *Calista,* she sat in her dressing-room her teeth fairly rattling. As she listened to the discordant orchestra droning out the overture, she was almost tempted to rush out of the theatre, dressed as she was; but the music ceased, the shabby curtain wound up in spasms of protest, the play was on its way and there was no drawing back.

A select few from the élite of the town sat in the boxes in stony silence. A scattered residue of workers in the spinning mills of Leeds spotted the pit benches here and there, languid and indifferent in the heat of the July night, monosyllabic in conversation with their sweethearts and wives. The only recognition of *Calista's* entrance was from a single pair of hands where Wilkinson sat. It was only too plain that Dora Jordan was terrified. Her voice, hesitant and uncertain, could not climb the barrier of inhibition that held it in bondage. Subdued giggles and coughs coming from the entrance, down right, caught her ear. She glanced off—three faces mowed and grimaced at her. The opposite side—another group pantomiming demoniac laughter. The cabal was at work.

Her fighting spirit came to her rescue. She managed her ensuing scenes with a show of vivacity and surety and avoided complete disaster. Wilkinson's determined plaudits at her exit were joined by a faint echo from one of the boxes and a voice from the pit shouted, "Cheer oop, lass! 'Twere nowt so bad."

In the succeeding act her nervousness returned—

grinning faces showed at every entrance to the scene. She nearly collapsed. Wilkinson was puzzled—there were a few hisses. Then her mind went blank, every part of her was numb. Wilkinson tore back to the stage in time to catch the conspirators scuttling away from the entrance doors and the situation was saved. She was growing surer with every moment. The icy audience was thawing.

At the end of the tragedy, Nicholas Rowe's FAIR PENITENT, after dying with extreme pathos to the squeaking of the fiddles of the orchestra, she donned a frock and mob cap and bounded on the stage to sing THE GREENWOOD LADDIE with such lively sentimentality as completely to fascinate her hearers.

The night was hers. Wilkinson was amazed and delighted. But she had narrowly escaped a debacle.

With other nights and other parts her path to success was made smoother—her enemies were routed. The business of the theatres at York, Leeds, Hull and other towns visited by Wilkinson's strollers grew appreciably and justified the manager's belief in his new-found genius.

Behind her shield of popularity the girl breathed a sigh of relief. Little likelihood that Dorothea Bland who, as Miss Francis, made her début three years ago in Dublin would be recognized now in the Dora Jordan of these North British towns. All that part was wiped out—done with for good. What a terrible nightmare it had been! She grew cold at the recollection of Manager Daly. He was like something stepped out of the old melodramas she had acted in, the villain of the play. How was she to know that this smooth-spoken gentleman, all grace and gallantry, who had been so solicitous for her welfare, so kindly in relieving the money distresses of her family, was plotting her seduction? She was but sixteen and her distraught mother had too many worries to face in providing for her nine children to safeguard the conduct of her Dorothy.

The child in her fool's paradise thought that Daly's hypocritical benevolence, his kindness in casting her for sentimental heroines of third-rate plays at the Crow Street Theatre, was but her just due. He had flattered her vanity with his lies about her talent until she fancied herself another Mrs. Siddons. She was not the easiest prey, however, even when the Dublin Machiavelli threatened her with jail for non-payment of money he had advanced unless she yielded. Daly was not to be denied. Promises, pleadings, menaces, an abduction to a lonely house and the girl was left to weep as others had mourned before her.

When Dorothy made her clandestine escape from Ireland she and her mother had but the vaguest idea of a city of refuge. They found themselves in Leeds, a grim northern city where scandal seemed unlikely to penetrate. Mrs. Bland altered her daughter's name from Francis to Jordan and presented her to Tate Wilkinson whose company was providentially filling a meager engagement. Wilkinson had played with Mrs. Bland in Dublin years before Dora was born and was kindly disposed to the lady's petition although he doubted that the prodigy could ever fulfill the lavish praise her mother heaped upon her.

After the unqualified approval of her first night's audience there remained no doubt in Wilkinson's mind. He was quick to see the value the girl added to the company. At a salary of fifteen shillings a week she doubled the receipts in his circuit of towns.

But the vengeful Daly had bided his time. In the very heyday of her popularity he appeared with a warrant of arrest for money loaned and for the forfeiture of a contract broken by her precipitate flight from Ireland, and from his slimy advances. Her piteous plight so moved a gallant Yorkshireman named Swan that he loosened his purse strings to the tune of two hundred and fifty pounds. Daly ground his teeth, took the money and with his best melodramatic scowl retreated to Dublin. A recorder of this episode relates that the honorable Mr. Swan remained Miss Jordan's sincere and disinterested friend. I hope so.

As her provincial fame grew, London, always hungry for novelty, inquired whether or no this favorite of the provinces possessed town quality. Emissaries from Drury Lane journeyed northward and brought back golden reports despite the carping criticism of Mrs. Siddons who witnessed her performance at York and said: "She had better remain there than venture on the London boards. She? At Covent Garden or Drury Lane? It is unthinkable!"

From the tower of her deliberate grandeur Sarah

Siddons could see nothing so small as little Miss Jordan. She was on familiar terms with the gods of Olympus and could only look upward.

Dora's genius for comedy was finding vent. The sobbing heroines of melodrama were thrown aside and her comic spirit was recreating the parts of *Romp, Priscilla Tomboy, Nell* in THE DEVIL TO PAY, *Lady Teazle, Lady Racket* and *Peggy* in THE COUNTRY GIRL. The latter part had been the *chef-d'œuvre* of one Mrs. Brown, a mirth-provoking actress in Wilkinson's company.

The sly Dora posted herself at the wings on THE COUNTRY GIRL nights and watched Mrs. Brown like a hawk, noting all the laughs she got, the details of her stage business, her reading, until she could reproduce the original and better it by a league. Her girlish artless hilarity won the day over the declining powers of the aging Mrs. Brown. She ignored the hissing mouths in the serpent nest of the company. The brilliancy of her talent scotched the venom. Her public and her management were with her.

Her London début in 1785 was in THE COUNTRY GIRL and her *Peggy* became the talk of the town. The Drury Lane management gave her every opportunity, even producing TWELFTH NIGHT for her appearance as *Viola,* which part she presented with a combination of pathos and gaiety that swept all opposition.

During the days of her early triumphs Richard Ford walked into her life with a show of sincerity that she accepted with conviction. He had popular-

Courtesy of the Harvard College Library, Theatre Collection

Dora Jordan as *Peggy,* the country girl

ity, good looks, fine manners, an easy grace and his father bore a title. It was a simple matter for him to tell Dora that he would marry her, equally simple to tell her later that his family opposed the union. Arrangements like this were rather popular in the Georgian theatre. Notwithstanding its irregularity the unblessed union lasted for some years and three little Fords raised a baby clamor within the family circle. But Dora Jordan had a certain regard for the proprieties, she insisted on taking the name of Ford herself, believing that in good time Sir Richard's opposition would wear away. The Bow Street magistrate was unrelenting, he would have naught of his son's mistress. Dora made a *moue* at *pater familias* and took the fortune of war with what grace she could. Now and then she went into a little tantrum and swore she would leave her lover unless he gave her a marriage certificate, but he readily placated her, introduced her everywhere as his wife, and she went on having babies with delightful insouciance.

The scandal had little weight against her popularity at Drury Lane. Her salary climbed by leaps and bounds, greatly to the dissatisfaction of Mrs. Siddons who regarded this hoyden of the "breeches parts" as wholly unworthy the plaudits that grew louder with each new character she represented.

One who did *not* join the chorus of praise was the venerable Kitty Clive. "Pooh!" said the old comedian to her companion as she tottered from her retirement in Twickenham to view the new phenomenon at Drury Lane, "a bantam pullet! The town would prefer me at eighty to all the youth of the theatre."

Rosalind was added to her list of parts. There was a novelty, an unrestrained gaiety with which she romped through the woodland scenes of As You Like It that welded the ties which bound her to an adoring public. The rival house over at Covent Garden made overtures to the new favorite offering to meet her own terms if she would leave the Sheridan-Kemble management at Drury Lane.

Sarah Siddons groaned. Her supremacy as the tragic muse must not be shaken by the antics of a vulgar comic actress. It rankled her penurious soul to see another commanding a salary equal to her own. Yet Sheridan was forced to pay it or lose the magnet that drew overflowing houses to his theatre. The satirists found rare material in this rivalry. A caricature of the day represented the money-loving Sarah with her pockets bursting with bank-notes reaching greedily with a "Give-me-the-daggers" gesture for a bag of gold thrust up from the infernal regions on the prong of a pitchfork.

Melpomene's crown of sorrow lay in the fact that Jordan had triumphed as *Rosalind* while her own essay of the character had met with distinct failure.

An enraptured versifier wrote:

"To comic Jordan's laughing eye
The tear of pity stole;
But in revenge she drew a sigh
From each spectator's soul."

And this epigram from Peter Pindar:

> "Had Shakespear's self at Drury been
> While Jordan played each varied scene,
> He would have started from his seat,
> And cried, 'That's *Rosalind* complete!' "

Even Hazlitt runs past his common conservatism in praise of her.—"Her face, her tears, her manners were irresistible. Her smile had the effect of sunshine. Her voice was eloquence itself; it seemed as if her heart was always at her mouth. She was all gaiety, openness and good nature. She rioted in her fine animal spirits and gave more pleasure than any other actress, because she had the greatest spirit of enjoyment in herself. Her *Nell*—but we will not tantalize ourselves or our readers."

Despite this panegyric, and much perfervid laudation elsewhere, Dora Jordan was by no means ideal in the poetic parts of Shakespeare. A streak of coarseness trailed through her acting. Her overwhelming magnetic powers carried her through the rakes and romps of comedy and farce. No one could resist the infection of her laughter, the merry sparkle of her eye. As to her voice she could do anything she chose with it and wring a laugh out of the dryest line.

What if *Rosalind's* and *Viola's* tenderness and delicacy were utterly beyond her compass? Her admirers were happy in whatever she did. For them the vulgar little creature could do no wrong. She set the fashion, her sister comedians copied her.

They copied her in everything except the essential spark that blinded criticism and dazzled the eyes of her worshipers.

Less debatable was her fitness for the character of *Lady Teazle* in THE SCHOOL FOR SCANDAL. Sheridan's heroine was a sprightly country wench whom *Peter* had married and remolded with difficulty into the woman of fashion.

"Zounds, madam!" cries *Sir Peter*, "you had no taste when you married me."

The original *Lady Teazle*, Mrs. Abington, always gave the impression by her schooled and formal manner that she was born to the purple, in spite of the fact that Abington had begun life as a street flower girl whom every one knew as Nosegay Fan. No such nice scruples troubled the Jordan. She sailed into the part on the swirl of her native gaiety and played her own self. What more could one ask?

By this time the small world of the London theatre had become a hotbed of revolt. Dora had an unhappy faculty of fomenting enmity, and her enemies were growing busy. Like moles they burrowed in the dark in an endeavor to cut the ground beneath her feet. The Lord knows they had material enough to work on! She was constantly obeying impulses readily translatable by the evil-minded into indelicacies, but there is no evidence that she did not play fair with the dissembling Ford. She more than kept up her end in household expenses. The fertile Dora bore him children, she took care of them. More—she took care of him.

The night of a new character or play wherein she appeared was certain to be the occasion of hostile demonstration in various parts of the house at which emissaries were placed with instructions to hiss their loudest. An occasional illness which caused her absence from an advertised performance was turned into the accusation of wilful debauch and violation of agreement, and it is astonishing how the eighteenth-century audiences took such breaches of faith to heart. Managers of provincial theatres where she appeared during her tours grew wary of contracts with her.

One night when she appeared as *Roxalana* in THE SULTAN her foes had succeeded in inciting a well-nigh riotous onslaught. At its loudest she stepped out of her character, advanced to the footlights and waited until the howls of execration subsided under the counter-attack of her friends.

"Ladies and gentlemen," she began, "I should consider myself utterly unworthy your favor if the slightest mark of public disapproval did not sensibly affect me. Ever since I have had the honor to strive here to please you it has been my constant endeavor to merit your approbation. I assure you upon my honor that I have never absented myself one moment from my duties but from real indisposition." Then with the irresistible Jordan smile she concluded: "Ladies and gentlemen, I place myself under your protection."

British love of fair play was not proof against that. The house was hers as she well knew it would be. In its heart of hearts her public knew its Queen could do no wrong. No one could make headway against the flood of her popularity. Her theatre rivals crept into corners to gnaw the bone of their discontent. Her evil genius, the persistent Daly, who had come from Dublin, determined to have audience with her and see the child that had been born to them, retired in complete defeat. Ford who, stung to mad jealousy by the attentions that were being paid to Dora by the King's son, had furtively joined the cabal, fled to France. He could not face the ridiculous plight in which he found himself. Again and again Dora had appealed to him to make good his promise of marriage. The rising sun of the Duke of Clarence saw the setting of that of Richard Ford. Rivals of the little actress, embittered beyond measure, sharpened their teeth on this new scandal. They could only rend themselves.

The parsimonious George III caught the echo of gossip running like wildfire through the kingdom, and there was the devil to pay at Windsor Palace. The young duke was haled before his royal sire whose bulging Hanoverian eye blinked displeasure upon the profligate while his fingers caressed the golden guineas in his pocket.

"Hey, hey, what's this—what's this? They tell me you're keeping an actress. Is it true, sir—is it true?"

"Yes, sir."

"How much do you give her?"

"One thousand a year, sir."

"What—a thousand! a thousand! You'll ruin me, you scamp. Five hundred is quite enough."

There is an apocryphal tale that the young Duke reported his father's dictum to Dora who took a Drury Lane play-bill, tore off the printed line at the bottom which read, "No money returned after the rising of the curtain," and dispatched it without comment to her protector. We must recollect, however, that this slander was circulated by the fair Jordan's mortal foes. She had need of funds. Her salary at the playhouse was large, but she kept a pretentious establishment and there were the mouths of a small flock of Fords to feed.

Her circumstances were eased in 1791 when through the death of a relative of her mother her combined income was swelled to three thousand pounds a year. His royal Grace of Clarence heaved a sigh of satisfaction. Hanoverian cash was hard to come at and grudgingly bestowed. The exquisite darling of his heart was housed in splendor, he could adore her with an untroubled mind and an unlightened purse.

And she was content—vastly content. She loved her royal protector. She was faithful to him. The fruitful Dora was at her most prolific period. A troop of little Fitz Clarences commenced to appear, crossing the breed of Hanover, all destined to glorify the pages of Great Britain's Catalogue of Peerage. This high connection has no effect on her industry at the theatre. She is as loyal to her public as to her prince.

But here, in spite of the acclaim that greets her, a numbing fear is creeping into her work that is fairly unaccountable. She is nervous. Even in the wings, costumed and sure of her lines and the burst of applause that awaits her, she shakes with alarm. Once before the foot-lamps her tremors vanish. She welds the ties that bind her public tighter. Her *Nell,* her *Viola,* her *Lady Teazle,* her *Peggy,* and the part of *Sir Harry Wildair* that Peg Woffington used to hold all her own, grow more popular than ever. Sheridan sees his playhouse at capacity on her nights and beams with satisfaction. Even the stately Kemble is subdued. He revives Wycherley's PLAIN DEALER. Dora is opposite his *Manly* as *Fidelia* through which character there runs a vein of pathos that shows Jordan at her best. Kemble exclaims with unwonted warmth: "She is absolutely irresistible! I could have taken her in my arms and cherished her, though it was in the open street, without blushing."

Sarah Siddons is quite scandalized at her brother's enthusiasm. It is not thus that the Kembles should behave. There is a vague reason for Dora's uneasiness. Her detractors have become more violent than ever. She is used to carping. She has been able to sleep o' nights in spite of it. But it is beginning to wear into her nerves. Popular views of princely amours have changed somewhat since the days of Charles and Nell Gwinn.

With ever ready sympathy she had come to the rescue of a poor widow and her children who had been thrown into a Chester prison for a small debt. After being freed the woman followed and caught up with her as she had taken refuge from a shower under a porch. Pouring out her gratitude the widow and her children fell on their knees. Dora made light of the affair, slipped a guinea into the woman's hand, and sent them away with a word of cheer.

A man stepped out from the shadows of the porch and extended his hand.

"Lady," said he, "would to the Lord the world were all like thee!"

Dora retreated.

"No, I won't shake hands with you. You are a Methodist preacher, and when you know who I am you'll send me to the devil."

"The Lord forbid! I am a preacher of the Gospel, but do you think I can see a sister fulfilling His commands and not offer her the hand of friendship?"

"No, I don't like fanatics, and you won't like me when I tell you what I am."

"I hope I shall."

"Well then, I am a player. I know you've heard of me. I am Mrs. Jordan."

After a moment, "Thy calling matters but little. If thy soul upbraid thee not the Lord forbid I should. He has given thee a large portion of His spirit."

The rain being over, the preacher offered his arm. They proceeded on their way, and Methodism unhinged its stiff neck as the parson bowed his respect over Dora Jordan's hand at her lodgings' door.

More and more did her domestic duties and her constant contributions to the future peerage of England remove the Prince's favorite from the public, many of whom were openly derisive as to the prerogatives of royalty. The Duke of Clarence might be the noblest sailor that ever sailed a ship, the flower of His Majesty's navy had no *droit du seigneur* in their own flower of Drury Lane. There were many disappointments, many cancellations of her appearance in her favorite characters.

One morning she flung herself through the stage door with a great show of petulance and began rehearsal of her part in a worthless comedy called CHEAP LIVING with but little of her usual graciousness. She didn't like her part and made no effort to pretend she did. Wroughton, the director, was annoyed. The season at Drury Lane had been disastrous despite John Kemble's efforts at magnificent production. Salaries were in arrears, the company disgruntled.

"Ah! we are the grand lady this morning," snapped Wroughton, "quite the Duchess."

"Duchess? Hmpf! Very like. You aren't the first one to call me that to-day. My cook has already honored me with the title."

"Your cook?"

"Yes, she's Irish. She forgot that I'm Irish, too. I discharged her. When I paid her wages she banged a shilling down on the table and told me she would get even. You should have heard her. 'Arrah now, honey, with this bit of a coin won't I sit in the gallery—and won't your Royal Grace give me a curtsey—and won't I give your Royal Highness a howl and a hiss into the bargain?' " Whether or no Miss Bridget's threat was carried out I know not, but Jordan's laughing success in the trashy piece served to make up some of the back salaries due her fellow players. It was not the first time she had been the season's salvation.

Little Fitz Clarences arrived with distressing regularity. The Sailor Prince was enchanted. Dora accepted her incessant motherhood with complaisance. The patrons of Drury Lane were in the doldrums. It grew well-nigh impossible to ride the refractory horses of acting and domesticity. They were continually pulling away from each other.

She was losing ground. Moreover she was growing fat. Though the unsanctified union progressed with nice understanding between Clarence and Dora, it provoked only execration elsewhere. To the common people of England it was a scandal, to the Royal Family an annoyance that was wholly unnecessary. Funds for the support of the ménage were slow to be paid, sometimes they were not paid at all. There were not lacking those who declared that expense for many of His Highness's pleasures was defrayed by Dora herself.

Only once does the Court condescend to pay a command visit to the theatre. Jordan is appearing in SHE WOULD AND SHE WOULD NOT, and is as excited as a country girl in the presence of all her left-handed connections. One moment she goes white and faintlike, and the next, enormously pretty, blushes red as any peony.

The Princesses are simpering behind their fans in their eagerness for the sight of their brother's mistress, and the young Princes are smiling cynically at the Sailor Prince who is trying his hardest to appear unconcerned.

George III enters the box amid loud acclaim while the band blares GOD SAVE THE KING, and as he bows to the ovation a shot rings out. The pistol that had been pointed at His Majesty falls smoking to the floor of the pit, and before the audience has recovered from its panic the would-be assassin escapes. All the Princesses scream and promptly swoon away, the Princes make a noble show of bravery and George III advances unharmed to the front of his box to show

> "There's a divinity doth hedge a king
> Let treason peep to what it would."

Dora Jordan with the prettiest of gestures stills the uproar and informs every one that the assassin has been "perfectly secured and properly attended."

"They are only firing squibs," remarked His Majesty to the Queen.

Royalty resumes its stiff and bored decorum and, to the credit of the house of Hanover, stick out the play. But it never again came to the theatre while Dora played.

Just one more piece of the Jordan ill luck. She was wearying of the vanity of the stage. Her appearances grew fewer. "I have played THE COUNTRY GIRL so many times that if my friends are not tired of the repetition I am almost ashamed of it."

Old Drury was totally consumed by fire in 1809. It had been twice rebuilt. Now its glories were in ashes; in them lay costumes, jewels, property of great value that had belonged to Dora Jordan. As she gazed upon the ruins she said, "This ends it all. I shall act no more," and she kissed her hand for ever to the London stage. For over twenty years she had served it faithfully, twenty years of unprecedented success, twenty years of heartbreak and calumny.

There were a few appearances—very few—at Richmond, Bath and Dublin where the glamour that surrounded the lady who had captured a King's son attracted the curious. She was sick of her profession.

"My success through life has been extraordinary. I have had great emoluments but ever since I was fourteen I have had a large family to support, my mother, my brothers and sisters, money has been lavished upon them. But I have lost those great excitements, vanity and emulation. The first has been amply gratified, the last I have no use for, and now——"

Her obligations became greater. Her huge and variously fathered family was growing up, and Ford had never made any provision whatever for his share in it. The royal pension was uncertain. For two decades she had mothered the swelling list of the Fitz Clarences and dedicated it to posterity—five sons and five daughters with the blood of Hanover in their veins.

When her daughters married she became the target for an onslaught of libel and calumny from the blackmailing press, the penny sheets and the infamous caricaturists of the time. There was no immorality or degradation that was not hinted at; she had deserted the Duke, the Duke had deserted her, she was throwing her favors broadcast, her children had disowned her. The poor lady was smothered under a shower of filth.

Her sense of humor was equal to it all. God had not given her that merry laugh for nothing. At Bath, where the scandal-loving fashionables had little to do except to play battledore and shuttlecock with the newest gossip, she entered the Pump Room to look over the papers. A knot of excited busybodies, quite unaware of her identity, were at the next table. Dora listened.

"I hear the King has stopped her pension."

"They say the Duke has declared her children none of his."

"My dear, I had it from one who was in the very room. Not only did His Highness show his disgust for the hussy, but told her never to dare address herself to him again."

"I saw her on the Parade this morning. Such a fright! An old lutestring gown that I should be ashamed to have my maid appear in."

"Oh, yes, I know her quite well, but I told her only last month I feared we must part company."

At that moment a lackey ushered a lady into the Hall and inquired for Mrs. Jordan. The astonished scandal-mongers saw a plump and charming little lady, attired in the newest mode, rise, almost beside herself with mirth, make them a sweeping curtsey and take her friend's arm out of the room.

"In pity to them," says Dora, "I left immediately, and flatter myself I did not show any disgust or ill nature on the occasion."

It was two years after this that the blow fell. The Duke of Clarence announced the definite end to their connection. It was not unexpected—the wonder was that Dora had held him so long. But it was a heartbreak. Nothing mattered now, not even through the five more years that remained of life.

Thus she records her grief at her house in Bushy in letters to a friend:

"My mind is beginning to feel somewhat reconciled to the shock and surprise it has lately received, for could you or the world believe that we never had for twenty years the semblance of a quarrel? Money, money, my good friend, or the want of it has, I am convinced, made him at this moment the most wretched of men, but having done wrong he does not wish to retract. But with all his excellent qualities, his domestic virtues, his love for his lovely children, what must he not at this moment suffer? His distresses should have been relieved before. All his letters are full of the most unqualified praise of my conduct, and it is the most heartfelt blessing to know that, to the best of my power, I have endeavored to deserve it. I have received the greatest kindness from the Regent, and every branch of the Royal Family, who, in the most unreserved terms deplore this melancholy business.

"The whole correspondence is before the Regent. He declares he never will forsake me. My forbearance, he says, 'is beyond what he could have imagined.' Had he left me to starve I never would have uttered a word to his disadvantage. . . .

"My dear friend, do not hear the D. of C. unfairly abused. He has done wrong, and he is suffering for it. But as far as he has left it in his own power he is doing everything kind and noble even to the distressing *himself*."

To her correspondent she remains
"my dear Sir
"Yours sincerely,
DORA JORDAN."

Two letters were enclosed "for your eye alone." The second from Bushy several days later:

"My dear Sir,

"I should be sorry the letters I have enclosed to you were the only vouchers I could produce to the world if necessary. But, good God! what will not the world say? I received two letters this day telling me that I was accused of intriguing with the Duke of Cumberland!

"I am heart-sick and almost worn out with this cruel business; but I am
"Very gratefully yours,
"DORA JORDAN."

The fifth and last of this series of letters:

"St. James's, Tuesday
"7th December

"My dear Sir,

"I lose not a moment in letting you know that the Duke of Clarence has concluded and settled on me and his children the most liberal and generous provision, and I trust everything will sink into oblivion.

"Yours ever,
"DORA JORDAN."

That this "generous provision" was provided is unquestioned and extended to the end of her days. But Dora's money transactions had become involved. Her story from this moment is a sordid tale of claims and persecutions. Pretended friends had secured her name to notes that were never met. Two of her sons serving their King in France were court-martialed for default in action. A daughter by Ford had married a man named Alsop, gone on the stage, and was later overwhelmed with difficulties. From all her children there was a clutch at her purse-strings. She could not face it. She fled across the Channel to Boulogne-sur-Mer to avoid arrest, and changed her name to Johnson. The adjustment of her difficulties was put in the hands of a go-between who involved them still further.

But through the windows of a little white cottage on the outskirts of Boulogne, she could watch the strip of sea that divided her from her own dear country. In the hush of quiet afternoons she turned her face to the westering sun, sitting in the shadow of the garden fruit trees and listened to bird songs in the branches and the hum of bees among the flowers. Madame Ducamp, her landlady, was kindliness and motherliness itself. An inertia that was almost peace overtook her. When the night dews called forth perfume from the flowers and filled the garden with fragrance she confided her sorrows to the stars and heard the echo of far-off reverberations as the edifice of her happiness fell, beam after beam, to the ground.

Her heart held no reproach for the man who had made a shambles of her paradise. She saw him always as glorified—a god who had deigned to dwell among mortals, for twenty years. The young demigods of their union would think more and more of their royal sire—but not of her.

"It is not, believe me," she said, "the feelings of pride, avarice, or the absence of those comforts I have all my life been accustomed to that is killing me by inches, it is the loss of my only remaining comfort, the hope I used to live on from time to time of seeing my children."

Soon, however, storm-clouds gathered, hovered over the little cottage and sent her hurrying to shelter farther away. On every side frustration rose like a nightmare, every vista of peace ended in denial. Perhaps no one at St. Cloud would know her.

She was ill, wretchedly ill. Everything should have been cheerful around her. On the contrary her very habitation at St. Cloud was a disease.

A discarded mansion guarded by two sentinel cypresses in a garden of weeds and rubbish near the palace square, rambling, gloomy, cold and repellent. One could picture it as the setting of one of Maria Edgeworth's tales of mystery wherein filmy shapes floated through dilapidated apartments and strange noises marked the hours of night. A long and echoing flagged gallery stretched from one wing of it to the other. Obviously it had once belonged to some noble of France, long since forgotten.

Here she was visited by an ancient admirer, Sir Jonah Barrington.

"I never could wander over the house at night," Sir Jonah wrote, "without a superstitious feeling seizing me. No English comforts solaced Mrs. Jordan in her latter moments, her chambers were shabby, the furnishings scanty and old. In her little drawing-room the best looking piece of furniture was a small, old sofa. On this she constantly reclined and on this she died."

That summer evening she lay in the darkened room listening to the mocking hoot of owls from the cypresses and the antiphonal honk of frogs in the pools. Before her tired eyes the page of the Peerage book with its list of Fitz Clarences unfolded itself.

1—George Fitz Clarence, Viscount Fitz Clarence, Baron Tewksbury, Earl of Munster in the Peerage of the United Kingdom, married Mary, daughter of George, Earl of Egremont by whom he has issue.

2—Frederick Fitz Clarence, Colonel in the Army and Aide-de-camp to the King. Married Lady Augusta Boyle, daughter of George, Earl of Glasgow and has one daughter.

3—Adolphus Fitz Clarence, Captain in the Royal Navy and Commander of the Royal Sovereign Yacht.

4—Augustus Fitz Clarence, in Holy Orders, Rector of Maple Durham, Oxfordshire.

5—Sophia Fitz Clarence, married to Sir Philip Sidney, eldest son of Sir John Sidney, Bart., of Penshurst Place, Kent.

6—Mary Fitz Clarence, wife of Lieut. Col. Fox of the Grenadier Guards.

7—Elizabeth Fitz Clarence, married to William George, Earl of Errol, hereditary Lord High Constable of Scotland, who has issue.

8—Augusta Fitz Clarence, married to John Kennedy Erskine, second son of the present Marquis of Ailsa, by whom her Ladyship has issue.

9—Amelia Fitz Clarence, married to Lucius, Viscount Falkland and has issue.

These, and the little lad who died, make up the illustrious ten, and these the former Duke of Clarence in 1831 invested with the title and precedency of the younger issue of a Marquis.

He was then William IV, King of Great Britain and Ireland.

For a time her last resting-place remained unmarked, then a flat stone appeared that was sacred to the memory of Dorothy Jordan. It tenderly described her manners, her wit, her charm, her benefactions and told the passer-by

THE DELECTABLE DORA JORDAN

She Departed this Life
The 3rd of July, 1816
Aged Fifty
Remember and weep for her!

Many did remember and weep. Others remembered and smiled in their tears. Among them I am sure was the critical friend who once discovered her charm.

"I have it, madame!" he said, "it is your swindling laugh. You have caught the hearty enjoyment of unrestrained infancy, delighting in its own buoyancy; and you have preserved this in children of a larger growth who in the world are checked and blighted by decorum and art, authority and hypocrisy."

There were those in England who swore that she did not die in distant St. Cloud as was reported. People who die strange deaths in out-of-the-way places have an annoying manner of returning to credulous ones, perhaps from the spirit world, after the recorded date of their taking off.

John Ort, Marshal Ney, the "Lost Dauphin" persisted in revisiting glimpses of the moon after they had been decently buried. There are many others who refuse to lie quiet in their tombs.

Dora's perturbed spirit, or its corporeal case, must needs return to Britain. Her biographer, Boaden, declares that one day after the little woman had been reported dead and buried at St. Cloud, she was met and spoken to by an intimate acquaintance on the street in London. A stoutish lady was gazing through a thick veil at some trinkets in a shop window. As she raised her lorgnette the observer recognized an inimitable gesture that could belong to none other than Dora Jordan. He waited, watching; she lifted the veil for a better view. Beyond question it was she. "Is not this Mrs. Jordan?" he inquired. The lady gave him a terrified look of recognition—was about to speak, then dropped her veil and hurried on. Others in her own family protested that they had met her. Who knows? London had been very dear to her. It is all strange and disturbing.

VII

THREE MADMEN OF THE THEATRE

1. George Frederick Cooke

VII

THREE MADMEN OF THE THEATRE

1. George Frederick Cooke

Among the souvenirs of dead and gone actors in the treasure vault of "The Players" in Gramercy Park—books, miniatures, laurel wreaths, gem-studded daggers and personal jewelry—visitors to the club are shown—a tooth.

It is held aloft by a gilt wire, attached to a small velvet covered base—as ragged and carnivorous a molar as ever served the digestive necessities of the Cro-Magnon man. It is a tooth that has crumbled many a choice confection of early New York chefs: oceans of good wines and vicious spirits have flowed past it. It has vibrated to the tones of a voice now dulcet and seductive and again shrill and raucous with passion: it has bitten into the blank-verse speeches of *Richard III, Iago* and *Sir Giles Overreach.*

Whatever remained of its owner was buried down in the financial district, and broker's clerks, messengers, new-landed immigrants, honking taxis and Broadway street-cars rush ceaselessly by what the decay and worms of over a century have left of George Frederick Cooke, lying behind the palings of St. Paul's churchyard.

Although there seems some doubt about his parentage and his birthplace, Cooke said his father was Irish.

We may easily believe that the fervor and romance in a boy of thirteen that caught fire at the sight of his first acted play indicated Celtic blood. There is a suggestion of Handy Andy in the tale of the unpremeditated entrance of young Cooke upon the stage in MACBETH. He had sneaked into the theatre at Berwick-on-Tweed and secreted himself in the big barrel that held the cannon-balls for the thunder of the witch scene. The property man on receiving his cue began rolling his machine when he was startled by hearing from within not only the reverberations of thunder but very human shrieks and yells. The effect of the "cauldron scene" was immeasurably heightened by the appearance of an unkempt lad who suddenly shot in among the witches bruised, bleeding and terrified.

Notwithstanding this unhappy experience he made himself a nuisance to various barnstorming managers visiting Berwick. Failing to find encouragement he fled from the town and went to sea; came back in disgust; failed dismally in a business enterprise; inherited some money—spent it; and finally in 1776 made his appearance at Brentford, playing *Dumont* in the tragedy of JANE SHORE.

From thence onward his life led him through vagabond adventures among villages, towns and then to the cities of importance in companies of increasing standing and respectability. He took his responsibilities lightly, riotously, alcoholically. During a whisky-crazed moment in Dublin he enlisted in the army and woke to find himself doomed to scullery work and the most degrading of barrack duties. He would have hanged himself had not friends procured his release. It was in Dublin that he encountered the stately John Philip Kemble, playing secondary parts to Kemble's *Hamlet, Richard* and *Lear*. Evidently his tipsy habits disturbed the illustrious visitor who complained that Cooke did not give him his cues. Cooke came back with: "I won't have your faults fathered on me! And hark ye, Black Jack, damn me if I don't make ye tremble in your pumps yet!"

On an October night in 1801 at Covent Garden he made good his threat. He played *Richard III* and Kemble was there to see him do it. If "Black Jack" did not tremble in his pumps his ears certainly vibrated to the thunders of applause the occasion brought forth. Leigh Hunt, viewing his performance, exclaimed, "He is the Machiavel of the modern stage!" It was no precocious youth who won his triumph that night, but a man of forty-five who had passed through the ordeals of success and failure, affluence and poverty, appreciation and neglect and whose iron constitution had withstood the inroads of wild orgies of drinking.

During the entire year the stimulus of his sudden popularity in London kept him comparatively free from the attacks of his old enemy, but in the season that followed his indispositions grew more frequent and more lasting. To make sure of his appearances his manager was wont to entertain him on his acting days, regulate his liquor supply and carry him bodily to the theatre: but George Frederick managed now and then to escape and leave no trace behind.

At times during his performances he was fighting drunk and disposed to take issue with the remonstrations of his hearers. At Liverpool he was once faced by a storm of protestations and cries of "Apologize." Standing before his hecklers, his eyes aglare and his voice thick with rage he shouted: "Apology—from George Frederick Cooke! Take it from this remark: there's not a brick in your infernal town that is not cemented by the blood of a slave!"

In those days Liverpool merchants waxed fat by carrying on a nefarious slave traffic.

Of all the strange individuals bred of the life of the theatre, none was more mad than Cooke. Doctor Doran referred to him as a "compound of genius and blackguard." There is, however, evidence that Cooke was rarely so lost in his mental aberrations as to be unable to control them if it came to a question of his personal security. His own analysis of his infirmity has a Hamlet-like turn in a confidence given to one of the pages of his journal. He wrote: "I am sometimes in a kind of mental intoxication: some would call it insanity. I believe it is allied to it. I then can imagine myself in strange situations and strange places. This humor, whatever it is, comes uninvited but it is nevertheless easily dispelled—at least, generally so. When it *can not* be dispelled it must, of course, become madness." Though it was madness yet there was method in't—it was too tempting a thing for his actor's temperament not to give full vent to his antic dispositions when he saw his public regarded them as the eccentricities of genius.

And yet the notoriety of his escapades was not often worth the money they cost. At Manchester he pocketed the four hundred pounds his benefit had brought him that night and proceeded to a public house where he fell into a brawl over politics with a group of tap-room loafers. On challenging one of the disputants, a tough little navvy with a square jaw, to fight, the fellow declined, saying: "Nah, Mr. Cooke, you challenge me because you are rich and you know I am a poor man."

"Do I! Then look!" said George, and pulling out his bank-notes he thrust them into the fire.

"That's all I have in the world. I am as poor as you are—and now, damn you, come on!"

But the fascination of his acting in his favorite characters was too potent to be resisted. George Frederick's very speeches of apology exacted now and then by an infuriated audience upon his reappearance after an unpardonable disappointment had so much charm and blarney that his hearers found themselves flattered into a state of perpetual forgiveness.

After a long term in prison for debt the prodigal

was given a tumultuous ovation on his return as *Sir Pertinax Macsychophant* in THE MAN OF THE WORLD by one of the largest audiences ever assembled in Covent Garden Theatre.

That Cooke possessed unusual powers as an actor can not be questioned. In characters of sinister nature he found his freest scope. In those of nobility and poetic dignity he was not successful. His *Hamlet* was inferior and after a second attempt he left it in the undisputed possession of his rival, Kemble.

It was indeed his only conspicuous recorded failure and came at a time when Cooke had been more abstemious than his wont and had risen to high popularity in London. Up to his *Hamlet* disaster he had kept a sober and conscientious daily journal of his habits and experiences. Shortly after, the diary comes to an abrupt end, one of his last confidences to it being a pathetic protest against his defeat. He writes:

"On Monday I acted Hamlet to a very numerous audience. Next day the newspapers, some of whom I believe were *prepared* for the business, attacked me in a manner that would have been deemed impossible to have happened to any one who had ever received the slightest approbation from a London audience."

On the night of the repetition of the play the unfortunate madman let down all bars to his fatal indulgence and was gloriously drunk.

At his best and in his moments of lucidity there

was much to be admired in him as a man. He was generous, manly, witty and a faithful friend. Though he had no foundation of education, he had an admiration and a hunger for knowledge and the literature of his time that led him into hours of companionship with books which he read with great discrimination. Knowing his weakness he constantly struggled with it, frequently tearing away from jovial company to give himself to long solitary walks in crowded streets or lonely country lanes, battling with his demon and filling his soul with high resolve.

He was an enthusiastic Tory. On an occasion he found himself in a dinner party with the impecunious William Godwin, whose hot doctrines of revolt laid eggs for future English Socialists to hatch. Cooke was especially amusing, and Godwin was entertained by him until the actor's loquacity spun out to tedious lengths, when the philosopher went sound asleep.

George Frederick, discovering that he was talking to unhearing ears, gazed earnestly into the sleeper's placid face and broke into apostrophe.

"Asleep. Fast asleep! How perfectly quiet he rests and yet he's a democrat! There is a smile upon his countenance that looks peace and good will to men, and yet he has thrown the torch of discord abroad and set half mankind in flame. What a beautiful head! How mild the expression as if he had been nourished on the milk of human kindness! What a head! And yet pregnant with monstrous errors that, if received, would destroy the bonds between subject and sovereign, parent and child, husband and wife; involve the world in anarchy and steep it in blood.''

He then evoked an anathema on all socialistic philosophers. ''But not him. O, no, no! His conscience is good or he could not sleep thus and look thus.''

He never conquered his real dislike of John Kemble who stood for all the Roman virtues and was in command at Covent Garden. On the eve of an advertised appearance as *Richard,* Cooke had his own costume secretly removed from the theatre, dressed for the part, and had himself driven to a place near at hand where he waited in demoniac glee picturing Black Jack's perturbation at his non-appearance.

The doors opened, the house filled, everything was in readiness for the play to begin but no sign of the truant. Kemble was pacing the stage in a terrible state of nerves, dreading the moment when he would go before the curtain and announce once more the ''indisposition'' of Mr. Cooke. The hour of beginning was past, the audience growing riotous, as British audiences in the early eighteen hundreds always became at any irregularity, when Cooke appeared apparently from nowhere and said quite calmly: ''Mr. Kemble, I am ready, sir.''

At his worst he sunk to the depths and was fit company for no one, Jekyll became Hyde, the fine-minded, courteous gentleman was transformed to the beast. Sometimes, as though performing an Eastern conjuring trick, he would fade completely from view, public and private.

In 1780 he disappeared for a whole year, vanishing like Macbeth's witches, into the air, leaving behind a rumor, which nobody ever proved true, that he had enlisted as a private in a West Indian regiment.

The elder Matthews, who later rose to great popularity in London, tells an absurd tale of a visit which he, as an ambitious beginner, paid to the veteran. Matthews had pleased Cooke by his conscientious acting in a play at Dublin and was invited to a tête-à-tête supper at the tragedian's lodgings.

It began with copious draughts of hot whisky punch which Cooke tossed down while delivering a harangue to young Matthews.

"You are young," he said, "you need some one to advise and guide you: there is nothing like industry and sobriety—another jug of whisky punch, Mrs. Burns! Dissipation is the bane of youth in our profession. Low company, villainous associates lead them from studying their business and acquiring the knowledge which alone can make them respectable. Another jug, Mistress Burns!"

His admonitions growing more and more maudlin he began a series of practical instructions in acting for Matthews' benefit. He showed him how the passions should be expressed in the face.

"What's this?" he demanded, making a horrible facial contortion.

The astonished youth said that it was very fine and remarkable.

"But what *is* it?" shouted Cooke.

"Anger," stammered Matthews.

"You're a blockhead—it's *fear*. And what's this?" making the same hideous grimace.

Matthews (hazarding a wild guess): "Hope."

Cooke: "Not at all—remorse! And this?"

Matthews (in great confusion): "Hypocrisy."

Cooke: "You lie—it's *love*—hear me, sir? Love!"

The night ended in complete riot, Matthews being driven out with the furniture of the room flying after him, chased by his mad host who spent the hours till morning in the streets and was brought home beaten, bruised and oblivious.

But Cooke's star, which had burned so brightly as to obscure the light of all his London rivals, was failing. The wonder is that it had held its brilliancy so long. His worshipers began to tire of seeing him on occasion mumble through a part with faltering tongue and mind bereft: weary of going to Covent Garden on his announced nights eager to fall under the spell of his *Richard, Iago, Shylock, Falstaff, Sir Archy, Sir Pertinax* or *Sir Giles Overreach* only to be met by the announcement that "owing to the indisposition of Mr. Cooke the play of the evening will be changed."

George Frederick found himself obliged to seek the provincial cities for support and for a livelihood. London engagements grew fewer. Even there he found himself for a time forced into the humiliating position of supporting Young Roscius (Master Betty) a thirteen-year-old lad who, like Lochinvar, had come out of the west from the County Down in Ireland, and was setting all London by the ears. Young Betty, a comely lad with a musical voice, had been carefully coached and acted the standard parts from *Hamlet* to *Young Norval* in DOUGLAS to the amazement of the public. There was a Master Betty craze; the prodigy became the topic of the town, and old favorites were forgotten. He was the Jackie Coogan of a day when theatres and players were few and far between.

Like many another craze, that of Young Roscius was of short duration: a season or two and the veteran favorites of yesteryear, Cooke, Kemble, Mrs. Siddons and others, crept back into preference once more.

The advent of George Frederick Cooke's appearance in America was the result of the unflagging determination of Thomas Abthorpe Cooper, an American tragedian who landed in Liverpool in 1810.

Cooper's story of his capture of the elusive Cooke reads like a chapter of a Sherlock Holmes tale. Affairs had gone from bad to worse with the actor; driven from London by the attacks of his enemies and the desertion of his one-time friends, he was filling an engagement in Liverpool, facing a future, furtive and sinister.

Cooke, hearing that Cooper was engaging actors

for America, remarked: "I might make the voyage myself should you think it worth while to tempt me."

Cooper hardly thought him serious but wrote to him a month later from London offering him twenty-five guineas a week for ten months in New York, Boston, Philadelphia and Baltimore, a benefit in each city and twenty-five cents a mile traveling expenses. To this offer Cooke made no reply, but when Cooper had finished his London visit and was passing by coach through Preston he saw play-bills announcing Cooke's appearance as *Richard* for the next evening.

He put up for the night at an inn, and when George arrived the next day brought up the matter of the American engagement. To his surprise Cooke told him that he knew nothing about it—had never heard of it. Accordingly Cooper took himself off to Liverpool to fill an engagement of his own. Meanwhile George Frederick after playing but two nights in Preston broke all the contracts he had entered into for other provincial cities, went off to the little seaport of Blackpool where for over a month be buried himself in debauchery and oblivion. Before Cooper had completed his engagement the manager of the Liverpool theatre informed him that Cooke was again in the city lodged at a low resort where he was "playing the madman, frequently very ill, and robbed at the pleasure of the wretches around him."

This was no time to enter into negotiations for America. To make proposals now would be to bring

From the Albert Davis Collection

Mr. George Frederick Cooke as *Richard III*

Cooke's creditors about him like a swarm of flies—perhaps send him to a debtor's prison: the managers of various theatres throughout Britain would attempt forcibly to constrain him to fulfill his contracts. Cooke must be abducted. Cooper waited.

Cooke took a sudden notion that his presence was needed in London—and made preparations for immediate departure. A post chaise was ordered; it came to his lodgings day after day and was as regularly sent away. Cooper held a saddled horse in readiness which was brought to him at each appearance of the post chaise, his purpose being to intercept the traveler some distance away from Liverpool. He grew weary in returning the horse to its stable and began to think Cooke would never take leave when one afternoon a watching scout informed him that the post chaise was really off on the London road. Bidding a hasty adieu to a party of friends he had invited to dine with him, he mounted and rode out of Liverpool by another route. Before he could overtake the chaise his horse went lame; he was kept fuming at a wayside inn while the object of pursuit drew farther away.

By good luck, however, he managed to hail a passing stage-coach and by a liberal bribe to the coachman succeeded in reaching the first stage of the journey, Prescot, before the arrival of the chaise. Hastily ordering food, drink and a room, he pounced upon Cooke at the moment of his appearance and invited him to supper. George, surprised and pleased at the meeting, readily accepted. The proposal of the American engagement was introduced, Cooke, warmed by hot food and generous wine, readily agreed to terms. Leaving his guest voraciously attacking the supper Cooper slipped out of the room—paid the driver of the chaise and sent him back to Liverpool with the intelligence that Mr. Cooke had changed his mind about going to London.

Late that evening another post chaise put out from Prescot, leaving behind to sundry inquisitive citizens of the town drawn to the inn by the arrival of two renowned actors and who had demanded to be brought into the presence of the great Mr. Cooke, the information that the destination of the vehicle was Warrington. No sooner were the last houses of Prescot passed than orders were given to turn about and proceed hot speed to Liverpool. Inside the chaise were George Frederick Cooke overcome with liquor and dead to the world, and the exultant Cooper.

Arriving sometime before midnight, Cooper boldly rang the bell of a certain suburban residence and with the assistance of a servant deposited Cooke within the security of Mr. Tawbuck's house. Having accomplished this Cooper set off to the city to inquire about sailing ships, realizing that he must act quickly or his uncertain prey would elude him. The three-day interval that elapsed before the sailing of the next packet was an anxious one. Cooke, fancying himself at an inn, was inclined to be obstreperous. It was difficult to preserve the secrecy of his departure.

Peril pursued the enterprise to the very end. Just as the ship was about to weigh anchor she was boarded by a revenue officer who refused to sanction her clearance papers because she carried a passenger not registered at the custom-house. He demanded that Cooke disembark. Adroit explanation and a sufficient bribe at length sent the officer ashore, the COLUMBIA dropped down the Mersey, and Cooper, watching from the pier, breathed a vast sigh of relief.

What the feelings of the unfortunate Cooke were no one knows, but we may be assured that when he awoke to what he was really in for—a voyage of more than six weeks and a long, long exile from England, they were far from pleasant. His own journal contains merely this entry: "On Thursday, October the 4th, 1810, embarked at Liverpool on board the Columbia, of and for New York, North America, and sailed out of the harbour immediately. The master of the ship (about 300 tons), Joshua Hazard, of Rhode Island. On Monday the 8th cleared St. Georges Channel, and on Friday evening, November the 16th landed at New York after a tedious and tempestuous passage."

From other sources we learn that when seasickness overtook him he cursed himself, Cooper and the world with every roll of the ship and wailed out sobbing regrets at having left his native land.

Ultimately his sufferings ceased. Followed day after day when he sat on the deck of the COLUMBIA watching the waste of the tumbling Atlantic and loathing his fellow passengers who had, during his illness, drunk up the ship's stock of spirits, leaving no solace for his thirsting soul but *essence of lemon.*

But the enforced abstemiousness is giving back health and vigor to his abused body, cobwebs are sweeping out of his brain: the voyage is drawing its weary length to a close and as the COLUMBIA glides through the Narrows of Staten Island Cooke can thank God he's in better fettle than he has been for years.

Safely housed at the Tontine Coffee House he is pleased at the visits of distinguished New Yorkers whom Mr. Price, the manager of the Park Theatre, brings to do him homage, and passes his first night in the new world in vast content.

He is not quite at his ease next day as he sets out from Mr. Price's house at 296 Broadway for his first view of the town. He has suddenly conceived a large contempt for the "Yankee-doodles." Albeit he is somewhat timorous he is certainly very curious about these strange Americans.

Few realize that this benevolent, rather scholarly-looking man, snowy haired, with a piercing eye that glances quickly to right and to left from beneath the broad brim of his beaver hat, clad in respectable English gray, high-collared above the folds of his immaculate stock, is the renowned London actor, George Frederick Cooke.

Mr. Price is tremendously proud of his convoyance, especially when, now and then, the passers-by show that they have recognized the celebrated man.

They near the Park Theatre: Cooke grows excited as he sees a group of people gathered about the play-bills that announce his forthcoming appearance as *Richard*.

As they draw closer they overhear certain cries of derision. Some Englishmen claim to have seen Cooke in London and are pooh-poohing the idea of his coming to America.

"The whole thing is just a Yankee imposition!" shouts one. "You might as well expect to see St. Paul's Cathedral transported across the ocean."

"The managers would never dare to do that," a man replies.

"Would they not? Those fellows would dare anything to gain a shilling. It's another performer of the same name. It's never George Frederick."

Price has some difficulty to prevent Cooke from dashing into the crowd and confounding them all by proclaiming his identity.

"I'll show your Yankee-doodles!" he exclaims as Price leads him away.

He is annoyed at a delay in the release of his effects at customs. At a reception tendered to him by many prominent citizens he can think and talk of nothing but the withholding of some valued cups presented to him in Liverpool. To every individual he complains about it: "They've stolen my cups—they've stolen my cups. Yes, and my Shakespeare. Well, they had better keep that: they need his instruction and may improve by him, if they know how to read."

Arrives the morning of November the twenty-first. The tragedian wakes early, extremely nervous, breakfasts on weak brandy and water and cold ham and after conning over the text from his prompt book of RICHARD III goes to the theatre for his last rehearsal. He is not wholly satisfied with the company.

"I could wish," he says, "that some of your actors were more correct, Mr. Price."

He dines at two o'clock, has his dish of tea at half after five, and shortly after seven that evening there is a hush, a thrill, and in a high state of nerves Cooke walks on the stage of the Park Theatre, the first actor of real power who has ever faced the American public. The throng at the avenues had been unprecedented; in the confusion many had been pushed by the crowd past the ticket seller and no payment received for them. Many ladies were taken around to the stage door in Theatre Alley and conducted to the boxes from behind the curtain. Twenty-two hundred people tax the little theatre to its utmost capacity.

Price and William Dunlap are gratified beyond measure.

"Look," says Dunlap, "how picturesque and noble he is; his eye flashing fire, his head erect. He steps like a conqueror. I see no vestige of the venerable old gentleman I met at the coffee-house."

Cooke returns the salutes of the audience like a victorious prince acknowledging an acclamation of the populace.

To many there is a sense of disappointment as he begins his soliloquy—

> "Now is the winter of our discontent
> Made glorious summer by this sun of York"—

in a sharp, grating voice, but soon he strikes his real pace, and before long New York has capitulated. The evening ends in a full triumph.

Doctor Francis in OLD NEW YORK, writing of Cooke says:

> "Old playgoers, by his expositions, discovered a mine of wealth in Shakespeare now first opened. His commanding person, his expressive countenance, his elevated front, his eye, his every feature and movement showed the great master who eclipsed all predecessors. . . . His master was nature and he would submit to no artificial rhetoric!"

Cooke had created a new era in American theatrical annals. Each succeeding night saw the Park crowded as the different characters in his repertory were displayed, and familiarity with his work brought new admiration.

Then came the change. Cooke failed to grasp his golden opportunity of starting life anew; under the stimulus of the admiration of riotous admirers he lapsed into his former habits and his "indispositions" once more became noticeable. On the night of his benefit he was well-nigh incoherent.

However, the receipts of his engagement had at that time never been approached in New York and George Frederick took himself off to the admiring throngs of Boston, Philadelphia and other cities. Honors were heaped upon him. Stuart and Sully painted his portrait. But always his evil genius was at his elbow luring him to fresh excesses and wild behavior.

On a day in February, after one of the coldest nights of the year, a little girl came to the office of the Park Theatre bearing a note which read: "Dear Dunlap, send me one hundred dollars. G. F. Cooke."

Questioning the child and learning that she had been sent by a strange gentleman at her mother's house, Dunlap set out with her to a mean building back of the Hospital. As they walked Dunlap asked his little pilot how the strange gentleman came to her house.

"Last night, sir, almost morning—mother is sick, sir, and I was sitting up with her—a negro and a watchman brought him. We knew the watchman so mother let the gentleman come in and sit by the fire. He didn't want to come. He said, 'Let me lay down here and die.' Poor old gentleman! It was cruel of the people where he lived to turn him out o' doors on such a night."

"Does he say he was turned out o' doors?"

"Yes, sir, I believe he is crazy."

In the chamber of the sick woman they found a motley crowd of people, cartmen, watchmen, neighboring women and children, gaping at the crazy man who stood among them spouting Shakespeare, denouncing American rebels, prating of patriotism and politics and bewailing some injury done to him.

On seeing Dunlap he burst into tears, begged him not to leave him, and swore he would never go back home where he claimed he had been grievously wronged.

In a corner of the room were several rascally-looking sheriff's officers who had drawn up lists of the sorry furnishings and effects of the invalid for a levy because of an unpaid quarter's rent. Cooke had gone security for the amount and declared he would not leave till it was paid. The debt being satisfied, George Frederick was led away followed by the gaping crowd.

The only explanation of this escapade Dunlap could uncover was that for some unknown cause, boredom, perhaps, or a fancied slight, Cooke had fled from his lodgings accompanied by Sam, his negro servant, and wandered through the ice and snow of a blizzard until discovered by the watchman.

One of George Frederick's delusions was that of having fought with the British troops in America against the rebels. He would describe how as an Ensign of the Fifth he drove Putnam from Bunker Hill and saw Warren die, or Sir Henry Clinton and his aides riding helter-skelter through Broadway, or an engagement between Lord Howe and General Washington at the storming of Brooklyn Heights wherein but for his lordship's calling a halt Cooke would have captured Washington.

During an engagement in Baltimore he was told that President Madison purposed coming from Washington to see him act. He flared immediately. Drawing himself to his full height he shouted:

"If he does I'll be damned if I play before him. I'll say to the audience, 'Ladies and gentlemen, the King of the Yankee-doodles has come to see me act—*me,* George Frederick Cooke, who have stood before my royal master, George the Third, and received his imperial approbation! It is degradation enough to play before rebels, but I'll not go on for the amusement of the contemptible King of the Yankee-doodles!"

But Mr. Madison did not come.

It was in Baltimore that a gentleman who had thrown open his house for Cooke's entertainment chanced to mention that his family were among the first settlers of Maryland.

"Indeed!" said George Frederick, "and have you carefully preserved the family jewels?"

"Jewels! What do you mean?" asked his host.

"The chains and handcuffs."

Cooke was doomed never again to see his native land. His will was becoming so weakened that he always failed to carry out the arrangements made for his return. His demon constantly held him in a stranglehold.

His physician, Doctor Francis, describes his appearance while under the influence of drink: "In that condition his whole nature was altered and his appearance almost diabolical. You dwindle under his indignant frown: no violence was like his, no obstinacy so invincible. On the return of his right reason he would cast a withering look around and ask: 'What part is George Frederick Cooke placarded for to-night.' "

Less than two years after he had set the American dramatic world aflame, his extraordinary vitality wore itself out, and death, which had watched so eagerly for him through the years, found him in the presence of friends who had stood by him in the face of all rebuffs and abuse, and the forlorn wife he had married in America and who had held but the smallest place in Cooke's life.

On the twenty-seventh of September, 1812, his remains were laid away in the stranger's vault of St. Paul's and New York held holiday.

It was not until June of 1821 that the monument that marks his last resting-place was erected in St. Paul's churchyard. Edmund Kean on his first visit to America, learning that his one-time celebrated predecessor was lying wholly forgotten in an obscure church vault caused the removal of the body and inscribed over his bones these lines:

> "Three Kingdoms claim his birth.
> Both hemispheres proclaim his worth."

The monument has at various times been restored by Charles Kean, the elder Sothern, Edwin Booth and the Players Club.

But poor George Frederick, who so often lost his head during life, was destined to lose it even in the grave. His friend and counselor, Doctor Francis, ruthlessly purloined it and he lies headless in St. Paul's churchyard.

There is a smug complacency in the doctor's description of an event of later date in OLD NEW YORK. He wrote:

"A theatrical benefit had been announced at the Park and HAMLET the play. A subordinate at the theatre at a late hour hurried to my office for a skull. I was compelled to loan the head of my old friend, George Frederick Cooke. 'Alas, poor Yorick!'

"It was returned in the morning, but on the ensuing evening at a meeting of the Cooper Club, the circumstance becoming known to several of the members and a desire being expressed to investigate phrenologically the head of the great tragedian, the article was again released from its privacy when Daniel Webster, Henry Wheaton and many others who enriched the meeting that night applied the principles of craniological science to the interesting specimen before them!"

If the boluses of the ponderous doctor were as indigestible as his literary efforts it is not to be wondered at that the unfortunate actor gave up the ghost.

Or is it possible that he talked Cooke to death?

VIII

THREE MADMEN OF THE THEATRE

2. Edmund Kean

VIII

THREE MADMEN OF THE THEATRE

2. Edmund Kean

In the forecastle of a ship that was driving through a Bay of Biscay storm, headed for the channel, her rigging torn, her loose spars flailing against her masts, lay a delicate undersized urchin listening to the groaning of timbers, the snapping of cordage and the pistol-shots of sails bursting apart in the gale. As the ship careened fathom-deep into water gulfs he gripped the sides of his bunk and dug his toes into the soggy mattress, his cheek ashen and his huge black eyes distended in fear. It was difficult to lie there acting a part, pretending that an illness had rendered him deaf, dumb and a cripple.

Yet acting he was. He had shipped as a cabin boy on the outward voyage to Madeira, dreaming dreams of gallant adventure, strange ports, tattooed seamen, fierce pirates; he had seen such glittering in the lamp-glow of the footlights and thought them true. The vision faded the first day at sea; in its place curses, starvation and the rope's end.

Not among the least of the successes of Edmund Kean was this assumption at the age of ten, of the rôle of invalid. He played it to a triumphant finish. He rode through the storm speechless and paralyzed and when the final curtain fell at Southampton he put his thumb to his nose and trudged off to London on the liveliest pair of legs in the world, singing as he went.

Yet he had no welcome waiting him at the end of the road—no home but the cheap lodgings of the mother who had brought little Edmund into the world out of wedlock, who had always hated and abused this evidence of her weakness. She had her living to make, a hard task for the inconspicuous actress that she was, and he was in the way.

So the child found himself in the home of Miss Tidswell. She had stood by in Nance Carey's lodgings the night that Nance had been delivered of the unwelcome Edmund and had fallen in love with his dancing black eyes. Miss Tidswell was growing a shade passé, but she still held her position at Drury Lane Theatre; her fine looks had not yet lost their charm for the Duke of Norfolk who protected her. So well housed was the lad that he used to think the Duke and Miss Tidswell were his father and mother.

But Nance Carey, during one of her intermittent returns to London, scented profit in her four-year-old son. She forcibly removed him from his comfortable home and secured engagements for him as apes, demons, and fairies in pantomimes. Nance had come far down the hill in descent from her grandfather, Henry Carey, famous as the composer of God Save the King and Sally in Our Alley. To be sure this particular Carey hanged himself in a fit of despondency, having previously gone quite to the dogs, but he had had his day of glory and renown, he could boast that he was the natural son of George Saville, Marquis of Halifax. Henry's son, George, was also gifted as an author, a lecturer and, in a small way, a player. He composed operettas, burlesques and interludes, and died poor. No doubt it was poverty that drove his good-looking daughter, Nance, into the life of a strolling player at the age of fifteen.

As to Edmund Kean, father of young Master Carey, there is little to say more than that he was handsome, graceful, Irish and a ne'er-do-well who drank heavily, lived riotously and went mad.

Master Edmund, after his long tramp up from Southampton, was by no means cast down to find his mother's London lodging empty. What matter where she had gone, there was always "Aunt Tid." Miss Tidswell welcomed her protégé with joy; once more he knew the taste of good food and the feel of cool white sheets. She taught him to recite and read Shakespeare to him. But even kindness and comfort could not ease his hectic spirit: occasionally he would break his bonds and run away to sleep in barns, to haunt wayside inns—imitating imps and apes, tumbling, dancing, reciting and singing for his bread and butter. That Miss Tidswell locked him in his bedroom with his school books made but little difference, he would wriggle down the water pipe at his window to wander for days; restless and uncontrollable as an alley cat. Even the device of welding on his neck a brass collar inscribed "This boy belongs to Number nine Leicester Square. Please send him home," had no effect; covering the fetter with his kerchief he defied detection and was happy. The poor little devil was used to shackles: when he was scarce more than a baby his reprobate father deciding that Edmund's scandalously bowed legs should be straightened clamped them into iron braces and in this state of torture sent him to be lodged with some humble acquaintance in Soho—a Mr. and Mrs. Duncan. Playing the Grand Inquisitor did not greatly appeal to Mr. Duncan. It disturbed his slumbers after his "four-ale" at the neighboring pub. He complained: "He used to sleep with me and my wife in his irons, *and they hurt us.*"

Little Edmund seems always to have been changing patrons. A Catholic lady, in whose chapel he served the altar, sang and, as Nance Carey expressed it, "threw the incense about." Then a Mrs. Clarke, who had taken a violent fancy to the slender wistful youngster whom Nance had brought to her home while peddling perfumes. When he recited the tent scene from RICHARD III to the ecstasy of a drawing-room full of her friends Mrs. Clarke capitulated completely and took him into her home where he knew luxury such as he'd never dreamed of.

From this stupid respectability Vagabondia called him. Once more he was clowning before gaping rustics in tavern yards and tap-rooms and starving for his pains.

Thus early did the boy become father to the man. The noble blood of the great Lord Halifax had been strained through too many generations of common stuff. But what the red stream had lost in conventionality and aristocratic tastes it had gained in fervor, imagination, creative power, that God-given quality we call genius. It burst into full flood in the veins of Edmund Kean.

Hitherto his talents had been poured out helter-skelter, scrambled and shot through a thousand channels with no knowledge of whence they came or whither they went. Now he saw the road to art opening before him; he wanted to act.

Through the influence of Miss Tidswell the regions behind the scenes of Drury Lane and Covent Garden became free to his access. It was a common thing for one of the cast of a play, groping his way to his entrance in the dark, to stumble across the fragile, eager-faced boy, his big eyes ablaze, his chest heaving with excitement, peering around the edge of a wing watching the majestic stride and lofty gestures of Sarah Siddons or listening to the melodious thunder of John Philip Kemble.

One morning Kemble, crossing the stage before rehearsal, heard shouts of laughter from the green-room. Inquiring the cause he was told, "It's little Kean acting *Richard III.*" Throwing open the door he beheld his company grouped about a shabbily-dressed lad who was spouting the speeches of *Gloucester* in *imitation of himself*. For this deed he was summarily banished from the theatre by the irate Kemble who possessed little kindness and no sense of humor. Twice he was sent to Windsor to recite before the King, Queen and the royal household. It is said that George III, always noted for his reluctance to part with a coin, so far forgot himself as to give him a guinea.

He soon found opportunities in strolling companies, obtaining his first chance with Richardson's show which frequented country fairs and races. Of this font of gaiety Fitzgerald Molloy writes:

"The manager was a tall man with a red face, dressed in high boots, crimson vest and a many buttoned green coat. The fair members of the troop, whose smiles sought to hide their lassitude, were decked with glazed calico, tarnished tinsel and tinfoil, clocked stockings and shoes that had lost all shape from long service. The gentlemen, fellows of infinite experience, good at turning a somersault, enacting a tragedy, cracking a whip or beating a drum were clad in vests and tights.

"Wherever the show went noise and merriment travelled in its wake. On the village green or at the races it was surrounded by rival booths, the habitations of dwarfs, mermaids, pigs showing complete knowledge of the alphabet, fat women and two-headed boys. In its atmosphere dwelt confusion begotten of the mingled strains of bagpipes, trumpets and fifes, voices of fruit venders, the report of musketry from shooting galleries, shrill cries of Punch, cheers from merry-go-rounds, roars from performing bears, shouts from the ballad-mongers and cries from struggling crowds."

Afterward we find him wandering with

Saunders' Circus performing with great skill as acrobat, tight-rope walker and bareback rider.

Not until he was sixteen did he become a real actor. He then pursued the life of an itinerant mummer for four years, happy in his privations, fond of his gipsy comrades, glorying in an occasional success, dodging landlords, escaping creditors, rioting, starving, studying—in love with life and fired with hope of the future.

At Sheeness, when playing *Alexander the Great*, his ear caught the derisive laughter of a box party. A witling cried out: "Alexander the Great? He's Alexander the Little!" "Yes!" shouted Kean in return, "with a great soul."

In Belfast he met and supported the Siddons. She arrived in Ireland with a formidable repertory, and Kean was given an important part in the opening play. Somewhat overwhelmed at the prospect he went on a wild debauch, was woefully imperfect on the first night, and the august one declared he had ruined her scenes. "Who is that horrid little man?" she demanded. On being told she prophesied that he had no future and would never make an actor. The "horrid little man" was destined to become London's pride when Siddons was a legend.

But there was yet a long wait. He did succeed in obtaining a London engagement at the Haymarket Theatre. It lasted but a short time and was remarkable for nothing whatever in Kean's achievements. He was soon back in the provinces, barnstorming, wandering from town to town, leaping from frying pan to fire in his contracts with one impecunious manager after another, pulling his belt tighter to stifle the gnawings of hunger, never losing his *joie de vivre* or the sight of his star.

In the midst of this hurly-burly the young madman married. It was not through motives of love and devotion: I fear there was something mercenary in his proposal to Mary Chambers—a streak of cupidity inherited, perhaps, from the importunate Nance Carey. The lady of his choice was a comely member of a Gloucester company, whose neat attire led Kean to believe she had money, a commodity of which he was always woefully in need. Before their honeymoon waned he discovered that she was ten years his senior and just as poor as he. But they faced their sea of troubles with fortitude. Never was a sea more tempestuous, more darkly overhung with the clouds of adversity. At times a bit of prankish humor would lighten the gloom, as when Kean, festering with humiliation at having to play *Polonious* to the *Hamlet* of a ponderous, passion-tearing actor named Smith, possessor of the leading parts at Swansea, unable to conceal his contempt at the idiotic behavior of the Court of Denmark, in the midst of the play-scene lifted his long gown and turned a double somersault, to the consternation of the *Hamlet* and the delight of the audience.

Journeying afoot the young couple seek employment in distant towns. The way is long, their legs are weary. He takes the lead, dressed from head to foot in blue, his dark face resolute, his jaws set, over his shoulder four swords from which dangle the family bundle of clothes. Now he looks back at the woman plodding weakly behind. Her head is buzzing like a beehive and her breast is heaving, she sinks to a bank on the roadside in hot suffocation, trembling and crying a little. Kean waits.

"Better now, old girl?"

"Yes."

"Come along, then."

It will be by the grace of God if poor Mary's baby isn't born in a ditch. There is a haystack to sleep under and on again next day.

Compelled to leave her at a shabby inn he jogs on, finding himself followed by a sinister-looking crowd who are making hot haste to come up with him. He recognizes the "press gang" seeking victims for service and bent on his capture. With desperation in his heels he tears through a hedge—across the fields, only to be confronted by a river. He swims the stream and, nearly dying with every step, reaches his destination. There, in a tap-room, he faints away, but is restored in time to go on in the tragedy and the afterpiece at night. The sparse audience yawns through his *Hamlet*, but they wake up at his dancing and singing, and scream with delight over his *Harlequin* in the concluding pantomime. In the next town the rustics do not relish his natural delivery and human impersonation of *Richard III;* the genius that flashes like lightning through his acting moves them not at all: they want their Shakespeare raw and roundly hiss him.

Turning from the scene with *Lady Anne* he hurls *Richard's* speech into their faces, "Unmannered dogs: stand ye when I command!" Again the yokels guffaw at his antics as *Harlequin.* He sickens to hear them. "I never feel degraded," he says, "but when I have the motley on my back. London—if I only could get there and succeed! If I *succeed* I shall go mad!"

The final goal is not yet—more dreary days—at last Swansea in Wales, and Mary, after traveling over two hundred miles on well-nigh soleless shoes, is brought to bed with a son.

Still no sign of London. They wander from pillar to post—striving and starving, knowing destitution, neglect and misery, unparalleled save by the heroic patience with which they are met by the sad-faced Mrs. Kean. Never ceasing to toil over his parts except when drink stews his brains, his energy is tireless. His wife tells that "he would mope for hours, walking miles alone, thinking intently on his characters. He studied and slaved beyond any actor I ever knew."

To add to their trials came a second son. In their black hour Kean cursed his destiny, and his poor wife prayed to God to remove her and her children from the light of day. It was easy to find the way to forgetfulness—over the bar of the neighboring tavern. Occasionally a rescuing party would tear him away from a knot of noisy roysterers and clear his head for his night's work, dousing it under the nearest pump until he nearly drowned.

From the Albert Davis Collection

Mr. Edmund Kean as *Richard III*

But Kean's reputation was growing, even leaking down into London where the addle-pated committee of Drury Lane were vainly seeking means to combat the growing indifference of the public for the theatre. Their treasury was in a sad state, there were no sufficient attractions to replenish it—no playwrights but bastard copyists of the Elizabethans, no tragedians but stuffed automatons who mouthed in ridiculous imitation of the grand-mannered Kemble and Siddons. Letters from Exeter, Swansea, Barnstaple, Tunbridge Wells and other towns to various members of the managerial body descanted on the merit of an extraordinary little man who could play *Hamlet* and *Richard,* dance on the tight rope and set the house on a roar by his antics as *Harlequin.*

While the august body deliberates on sending an investigator to bring report of the prodigy, Kean is tramping over a snow covered road to Dorchester, his swords and shabby costumes in hand, on his back the baby Charles. Howard, the elder boy, shivering and coughing in the bitter wind, pulls his thin jacket across his tubercular chest and drags after his mother who is laden with household paraphernalia. Not till the evening of the fourth day of their pilgrimage do they see the welcome lights of Dorchester. Drawing on his meager salary from the local manager Edmund procures a hot supper and a shelter, and in the warmth of a crackling fire the family forgets its woes in the always impossible dream of success to come.

Alas! this Dorchester is like all the other towns. The small audience sits frozen in the chilly theatre and makes no sound until the pantomime.

While washing the clown white from his face a knock comes at his dressing-room door.

"Who is it?"

"Mr. Samuel Arnold, acting manager of Drury Lane Theatre."

Throwing a ragged dressing-gown over his costume he receives his visitor in silent amazement.

"I have come up from London to see your acting, Mr. Kean."

Kean stammers an inarticulate acknowledgment of the great man's condescension.

My God! why couldn't he have let me know? And I playing the fool, and gagging all through the tragedy!

He is further amazed to receive from Arnold a definite offer of an engagement.

"For Drury Lane?"

"For Drury Lane. We will give you eight guineas a week for the first season, nine the second and ten the third. Or, should you prefer it, you may choose your opening character, and after you have played six different parts we'll decide the terms of contract."

Eight guineas! Is there so much money in the world? He will accept the first proposal. The interview ends. Kean sinks back in a daze. London! Success! Will it be madness? For many nights there is no sleep for Kean. His days are spent roaming on country roads—thinking—thinking hard. He even neglects the tavern bar.

What is there in London for him to fear? Whom among the aristocrats of the playhouse who amble through the Georgian comedies rapping their snuff-boxes, preening their ruffles in the manner of the fops and the Admirable Crichtons of the period? There isn't a tragedian among 'em! The Kembles are growing musty. George Frederick Cooke who had played so hard with fortune, winning and losing, has taken himself overseas to drink himself to death in America. If Howard only gets well we'll all be happy yet. But the poor lad can not get well. For many weeks while Howard lies slowly dying Kean acts, sings, dances, tumbles about in pantomime with a breaking heart, and gives lessons in fencing to a few young bucks of Dorchester Town.

Then came a foggy London night in January, 1814. Kean had thought that night was never to come. He had been subjected to every humiliation. The committee had lost faith in him. Aspirants for favor had been put forward one after another only to meet with failure. Still his opportunity never offered. No one could believe that this pale, ill-clad, woebegone creature could restore the drooping fortunes of Drury Lane. Then, too, the committee accused him of double dealing. Elliston, the manager of the Haymarket Theatre, came forward with the claim that he had made a previous agreement to act at that house. On this discovery the committee refused to pay him his salary. He could do nothing but haunt the stage entrance, sitting in the porter's room waiting vainly for a word of explanation with Arnold, who, when he did see him, passed Kean with a frown.

The actors going in to rehearsal view him with enormous amusement. A dame in furs adjusts her lorgnette and asks: "Where did they pick up *that* little wretch?"

"Look at the little man in capes!" chirps a sprightly comedienne.

Munden, the fat comedian, good naturedly says, "Go in front, my son, improve your evenings by witnessing *good* acting."

Stung and humiliated, but not crushed, he returns to his bleak lodgings in Cecil Street where Mary and the baby have been existing God knows how—on air, perhaps—and cries, "Let me once set my foot before the floats and I'll show them what I am."

Her faith is as strong as his, her love greater.

"Ah, Edmund," she replies, "those Drury Lane folk only see your little body, they don't know what you can do with your eye."

He tries to keep his reason in its seat until his time shall come. It arrives. Arnold, in desperation, capitulates and calls him to his office.

"Mr. Kean, we have decided to give you a trial. You will appear next Friday as *Richard.*"

"Thank you, Mr. Arnold," Edmund returns, "but that is impossible. I must open in THE MERCHANT OF VENICE."

"What! You—you——"

"*Shylock* or nothing, Mr. Arnold." He will take no chances on exposing his diminutive figure in the royal robes of *Gloucester.* His very effrontery robs Arnold of speech. In the end the "shabby little man in capes" has his way.

Rehearsals begin. Hardly any one pays attention to them. Several members of the company send excuses—they are ill and can not attend. Those who come mumble through their speeches, spiritless and bored. Kean reads the lines of the *Jew* in a low voice, giving no indication of what he is proposing to do with the part. Suddenly he startles every one with a flash of spirit—a glimpse of a vital, human *Shylock* that has never before been seen. There is a pause. The actor rehearsing *Tubal* has his lines knocked out of his head. Raymond, the stage director, is frightened.

"Mr. Kean," he says, "this will never do. It is quite an innovation: it can not be permitted."

"Sir," replies the little man, "I wish it to be so. If I'm wrong, the public will set me right."

The men glance at one another and turn their backs, the women snicker behind their fans.

The night of the twenty-sixth is one of the worst of the winter. Vehicles can scarcely get about through the snow, and foot passage is perilous. Edmund plows his way from his garret through the black slush, a few necessary properties in his hand. Outwardly he is very calm—he has dined for the first time in many days. As he kisses his wife at parting he says, "I wish I were going to be shot!"

Arriving at the theatre he is given a dirty, ill lighted dressing-room. He will have none of it. He chooses the supers' room, there dons his gabardine and waits. There is a thin and scattered audience in front—nobody in the boxes—few in the pit.

A player peering through a hole in the curtain remarks, "It's a shy domus."

"What do you expect?" says another, "there'll be nothing until half price—Jack Bannister's farce, that's what they want."

Kean walks up and down in the gloom back of the scenes. Bannister, passing him on his way to his dressing-room, wishes him good luck. Oxberry, the comedian, offers him a glass of wine. Nobody else notices him.

The curtain rises, presently comes *Shylock's* scene. To the usual conventional applause Kean returns a graceful bow, then forgets his audience. He has only one friend in front—Doctor Drury, head master of Harrow. At his first line—"Three thousand ducats?—Well?"—the doctor draws a breath of relief. "He's safe!" he says.

At *Shylock's* retort to *Bassanio's* assurance of safety of the loan—"I *will* be assured I may"—Doctor Drury's ears are gratified by a spontaneous applause from all about him. The act ends with the audience keyed up and expectant. The actors in the wings are still incredulous, waiting the damnation they feel sure will fall on the head of the shabby man from the provinces. Whoever heard of the part being played in such a natural colloquial manner?

"Look at the little beggar," says one, "he's playing it in a *black wig.*"

"Hah!" growls Munden, inhaling a pinch of snuff, "no doubt he's a marvelous entertainer. I hear he's a great tumbler."

"No doubt of it," replies the genial Jack Bannister, "for he has jumped over the heads of all of us."

The tension of the evening grows greater—the applause is incessant and when in the court scene, *Shylock,* crushed, humiliated, seething with suppressed fury, and turning like a wolf at bay on his tormentors at his exit—falls weakly through the door and out of sight—the tumult is deafening.

"How the devil," says Oxberry, "can so few of them kick up such a row?"

Before long the censorious crowd back of the curtain change their tune—they attempt gauche compliments; Arnold, who had for so long treated him like a dog, offers congratulations; Raymond, who told him he wouldn't do, presents a cup of negus; another, Pope, seizes his hand and vows he has saved Drury Lane from ruin.

Kean receives it all unmoved—he murmurs a few replies—slips from his gabardine and plunges back through the snow, his blood pounding in his veins, flies up his garret stairs and clasps his wife in his arms, shouting, "Mary, you shall ride in your carriage yet."

turned up to exact a pension of fifty pounds a year from her not too overjoyed offspring.

At home Mary Kean still trembled for fear she would wake to find it had all been a splendid dream. And if it was not a dream had she not the greater cause for fear? What had her vagabond Edmund to do with these great folk? Will success really make him mad? She even longs for the days when they starved and he was all hers.

For seventy nights he played *Shylock, Richard, Othello* and *Iago,* winning fresh laurels with each new appearance, daring in his originality and defiant of all the stale stage traditions.

Coleridge said of him, "Seeing Kean act is like reading Shakespeare by flashes of lightning."

"He is a relict of romance," cried Keats, "a posthumous ray of chivalry and always seems just arrived from the camp of Charlemagne."

For one hundred and thirty-nine consecutive nights prior to his appearance Drury Lane had been operated at a loss. The profits of Kean's seventy nights were seventeen thousand pounds. Small wonder that Committeeman Whitbread said, "He is one of those prodigies that occur once or twice in a century."

A second season strengthened his supreme popularity. He appeared for the first time as *Sir Giles Overreach.* The theatre was packed with an audience that tingled with expectancy. Kean's performance went beyond even their eager hopes. Lord Byron and Tom Moore watch from a proscenium box, Moore inclined to be somnolent after the long bout with last night's port; Byron is leaning over the box-rail, his poetic soul ablaze, forgetting even to pose his classic profile for the ravishment of his feminine worshipers. Carried along by the actor's performance he abandons himself wholly to its spell until his nerves snap and he falls from his chair in a dead faint. A din of cheers and bravos mark the final curtain. Kean has made another character his own.

Mrs. Kean has been too anxious to go to the theatre.

These first nights are terrible things! Much better stay at home even though you can only look out into the dark, suffer and wait. It is long after midnight when she hears a clatter of wheels on the cobbles and sees, through the window, the flicker of lanterns below. There is a noisy leave-taking with friends who have insisted on seeing him home.

The coach rattles off. Kean flings himself into the room and Mary hurries to him to learn the news.

"What did Lord Essex say?"

"Essex? Pooh! Damn Lord Essex! Mary, the pit rose at me!"

The succeeding seasons see the crushing of all attempts at rivalry—he reigns supreme. At the dinners and receptions tendered to him, however, he does not play his part so well. He wears his popularity with ill grace, awkward and self-conscious. Not till he escapes to the brawling of his tavern mates does he throw off his restraint. Surrounded

Following this debacle he reappeared as *Richard* and faced the most hostile demonstration he had ever known. The performance was stopped by howls of derision and exasperation—threats were shrieked at him from the boxes and the pit, and oranges were hurled at him—the vilest names in the British category applied to his character. English virtue had been outraged. The riot continued for many nights at Drury Lane and finally died out, but Kean was left a broken-minded man. To forget his woes he sailed for America where he was amazed to find the story of the scandal had preceded him. Riot ruled over the opening night in New York; through the yells and cat-calls not a word of *Richard III* was heard from beginning to end. Late in the season he journeyed to Boston for a projected engagement. Here he found an indifferent public and no advance sale. On the night of his advertised opening he looked through a hole in the curtain and seeing but a disconsolate handful of people he ran out of the theatre to the home of a friend and refused to make any appearance at all in Boston.

The following day a leading newspaper advertised ONE CENT REWARD for the apprehension of "a stage player calling himself Kean. He may be easily recognized by his coxcomical Cockney manners, his misshapen trunk and his face which is as white as his own froth. All persons are cautioned against harboring the aforesaid vagrant, as the undersigned pays no more debts of his contracting." This was signed "Peter Public."

Admiration for his acting was, however, too strong to be overcome by nice scruples; Kean returned to England immensely richer in pocket.

Five years before, in 1820, he had appeared in America and was received with the greatest honor and respect. Press and public were moved to ecstasies by his acting and he was hailed as the greatest dramatic genius of his age.

From his second visit Kean bore home one memory which he cherished to his last day. During a tour in Canada he had been introduced to a tribe of Huron Indians, invested with savage regalia and made a chief of the tribe. This honor he valued more highly than all the triumphs he had achieved at Drury Lane.

The years of decline set in. From his great eminence he saw his sun slowly setting, nor could an occasional flash of the most brilliant and vital acting he had ever achieved cause it to stand still. A year before the end Doctor Doran wrote of his performance of *Richard:*

"The sight was pitiable, genius was not noticeable in that bloated face, intellect was all but quenched in those once matchless eyes, and the power seemed gone despite the will that would recall it."

Out at Richmond when the days are warm and bright a wisp of a man, enveloped in mufflers and long coat, may be seen walking slowly across the green on the arm of his servant. To the grand folk he bestows a stately bow, to the common people and the poor a smile. The village urchins stop to stare as he passes. They tell each other: "That is Mr. Kean, the great actor."

The advertisements of Covent Garden Theatre for a night in March of 1833 announce his appearance as *Othello* to the *Iago* of his son Charles, now risen to a position of the first rank. Kean has gone early to the theatre—leaving word with the stage doorman to send his son to his dressing-room at the moment of his arrival. There is a long interval, and when Charles arrives he finds his father, haggard, wild-eyed, a shadow of his former self, mumbling incoherently and shivering over a fire. As the young man closes the door the shattered veteran of many campaigns, prematurely old at forty-six, raises a bloodshot eye: "You have come, my dear boy. It's very cold here. Charles, I am ill. I fear there will be no performance to-night."

Charles reassures him and orders stimulants. Some hot brandy and water restore him. As the moment of commencing nears something of the old Kean emerges from the shrunken figure and swollen face. The overture ends and the huge curtain rolls up. The audience wait impatiently through the first scene, then when the two Keans appear together the crowded house breaks into rapturous greeting. Edmund is almost too weak to withstand the emotion of the moment. With tears in his eyes but with his old, fine dignity he leads his boy down

My Dear Madam / I have been very ill & damned busy — so could not write we have been acting or travelling every night since we left London — I am going to Cheltenham & Bath two of the most notorious places in the world for fashionable fooleries. the Women painted faces & false breasts without hearts. the women men with false calves, stayed bodies & barbarously curled wigs. — the devil will have them at last from one of these Elysiums — I shall send the pocket book.

Yours very affectionately
E Kean

A most extraordinary Letter of Edmund Kean to Miss Tidswell

to the footlights and presents him to the public. Cheers shake the building, play-bills, hats, handkerchiefs and sticks are waved. It is a moment to remember.

The play proceeds. Kean is growing perceptibly weaker in spite of repeated doses of brandy. There is a forecast of disaster in Kean's request to his son to stand by him in the third act to help him to his feet after his kneeling oath. An unexpected autumn glory fills his voice as he reads *Othello's:*

> "Farewell the tranquil mind. . . .
> Farewell: Othello's occupation's gone."

A hush—the audience sob unashamed, then a storm of applause. He seems not to understand this—a bewildered look comes over his face: almost like one walking in his sleep he continues. Seizing *Iago* by the throat he commences:

> "Villain, be sure thou prove——"

He can go no further. Falling on his son's neck he gasps: "Oh, God! I'm dying, speak to them, Charles."

This was Kean's farewell to his public.

It was a long twilight—more than a month. In Richmond he watched the spring come outside his bedroom window, clouds chasing through his brain, clearing now and then.

In a lucid interval he wrote to his estranged wife:

"Dear Mary,

"Let us be no longer fools. Come home: forget and forgive."

With a love in her breast that was as much a mother's as a wife's Mary came. She had heard all, but she dared not come before.

Outside old Richmond Church there is a tablet which tells the passer-by that beneath it lies

EDMUND KEAN
Died May 15, 1833
AGED 46

It marks the spot where for the first time peace had come to the troubled soul of a man who was perhaps the greatest genius the English-speaking stage has ever known.

If you go there look carefully: long grass is growing about the stone and the lettering is very faint.

IX

THREE MADMEN OF THE THEATRE

3. The Elder Booth

ing little but discouragement, and in the following May he sailed with Jonas and Penley's troupe for Amsterdam on board a Dutch lugger.

An early biographer describes young Booth in the hold of this vessel when he first beheld him—"A handsome youth with a look that betrayed no ordinary degree of intelligence, seated astride a barrel eating a meat pie and shouting, 'By Holy Paul, I will not dine until his head be brought before me!' "

His fortunes were not bettered by this Netherland experience although he rose in rank among the itinerants until he was given the opportunity of appearing as *Richard III.* He arrived in England in April, 1815, practically penniless, accompanied by a pretty young wife who had eloped with him from under the nose of her objecting mother, a French milliner in Brussels. Although a marriage ceremony had been performed at Ostend, the knot was tied tighter by a second wedding at St. George's-Bloomsbury when the pair reached London. This marriage appears to have been the result of youthful impulse and did not last. Booth deserted his little Belgian bride, Mary Christine Adelaide Delannoy, and later took to wife Mary Ann Holmes.

Affairs now moved quickly. Booth had been seen and his acting noted by critical eyes. After some tentative summer engagements in the provinces, he was established as a member of the Covent Garden Theatre Company in London at a weekly salary of two pounds. During his second season at this house he was given his chance in his favorite part of *Richard III.* He appears to have been eminently successful and as often happens in the theatre, his success went to his head.

He began to squabble with the management. He was underpaid. What had genius capable of setting the town by the ears, as *Richard* had done, to do with two pounds per week? He would have none of it.

In the midst of the row, the great Kean swooped down upon him and bore him off in his carriage to the rival house in Drury Lane where the committee at once signed him on at a salary more commensurate with his position. Scarcely was the ink of the agreement dry than plans were put forth for the joint appearance of Kean and Booth at Drury Lane Theatre as *Othello* and *Iago.* The occasion was notable—the theatre was packed with an excited audience. Kean outdid himself in an evident effort to obscure his young rival by his own brilliancy as *Othello,* and Booth bore himself bravely as *Iago.* It must be remembered that the new aspirant to fame was but twenty years old and had had but a four seasons' knowledge of acting.

Against him was pitted the experience of a veteran and the worship of a host of fanatic adorers for their idol. In the reflection of the next day Booth came to his senses. He rubbed his eyes and examined his contract. To his consternation he discovered that he had agreed to play only the supporting parts to Kean—not one of his own favorite characters would be allowed to him. What a fool he

At succeeding appearances the opposition slowly subsided. Determination and the thick skin essential to those who pursued the actor's calling a century ago won through, and Booth stood more securely on his London pedestal.

At the end of three years that were significant in his triumphs and also for the beginning of his mental aberrations he sailed for America.

This truly was a land of liberty for him—here was no cabal—no precedent, no rival and, above all, no punishment for whatever antic disposition he chose to put on—whatever wild debauchery.

Landing at Norfolk with his new wife and a piebald pony he had bought before sailing from England he proceeded to Richmond, where he found a company playing, and at once effected an arrangement to appear with them. His reputation had come over the seas and on the sixth of July, 1821, the house was packed for the opening night of his favorite *Richard*.

During the earlier acts the audience showed a distinct disappointment in his acting and began to think it was an impostor who had assumed the name of Booth. He was going through his lines with the utmost indifference. The inertia engendered by a forty-four day voyage in a schooner was a handicap he could not at once throw off. His land legs wouldn't behave, and he was evidently confused by his new environment. Suddenly in the fourth act of the play his old fire returned and the audience was electrified. Never before had a Richmond audi-

From the Albert Davis Collection

Mr. Junius Brutus Booth as *Richard III*

ence seen acting so overwhelming as was presented by this little man who had landed on our shores quite mysteriously and unheralded. The city seethed with a new sensation. After four nights he accepted an offer from Petersburg. Ludlow, a member of the company in that town, describes his astonishment at his first sight of the celebrity:

"The play was called for rehearsal at ten o'clock, A. M. At the proper time they commenced but Mr. Booth had not arrived. The manager said the rehearsal must go on. I think the fourth act had been reached when a small man whom I took to be a well-grown boy of about sixteen years came running up the stairs wearing a roundabout jacket and a cheap straw hat, both covered with dust, and inquired for the stage manager. Mr. Russell on observing him hurried toward us and cordially grasping the hand of the strange man exclaimed: 'Ah! Mr. Booth, I am glad you have arrived. We were fearful something serious had happened to you?' No man was ever more astonished than I was just then at beholding this meeting. I began to think Russell was trying to put off some joke upon us. Is it possible this can be the great Mr. Booth that Russell says is undoubtedly the best actor living! He ran through the rehearsal very carelessly, tried the combat in the last act twice and it was all over. Then he said that being late for the stage-coach from Richmond he had walked all the way—twenty-five miles."

By the second of October we find him playing in New York and astounding the town by his acting, which fitfully veered from a languid indifference to blazes of force and passion. At times he seemed far away from his character, as if his mind were fixed on some thought utterly foreign to his playing, and suddenly in a confusion he would find his way back and hurl himself madly into the hot turbulence of the scenes of tragic action, swept along by an emotion that struck terror to the actors playing their scenes with him and electrifying his auditors.

At the Bel Air farm he withdrew himself from all thought of fame and public life. He became a simple country gentleman devoting himself to his crops and his cattle. In 1825 a desire to return to London seized him. He crossed the ocean in twenty-nine days and immediately opened at Drury Lane Theatre in BRUTUS. For two seasons he was received in Great Britain, Ireland and the Netherlands with great acclaim—but the voice of his adopted country was continually at his ear, and in March, 1827, he was acting again in New York.

From this period strange moods of forgetfulness and frenzy began to seize hold upon him—he had spells of heavy drinking with all kinds of outlandish companions and frequently, when advertised for an appearance, would disappear entirely for days. Then he would return to his playing with renewed vigor and feverish excitement, or more often, with a gentleness and calmness of manner as if nothing untoward had occurred. Sometimes on these occasions he would be utterly unable to give any account of himself.

The tragedian, James E. Murdock, tells of his own sensations on playing for the first time with Booth as young *Wilford* in THE IRON CHEST. Murdock at that time had had but little experience with the theatre and was ill prepared for the overwhelming personality of the star. Describing the scene where *Sir Edward Mortimer* discovers *Wilford* searching the mysterious chest he says:

"I had proceeded so far as to open the chest and trembling on my knee awaited the appointed cue for action. The time seemed an eternity, but it came at last. The heavy hand fell on my shoulder. I turned and there with the pistol at my head stood Booth glaring like an infuriated demon. The fury of that passion-inflamed face and the magnetism of the rigid clutch upon my shoulder paralyzed my muscles, while the scintillating gleam of the terrible eyes, like the green and red flashes of an enraged serpent fixed me spell-bound to the spot. Bewildered with fright I fell heavily to the stage tripping Mr. Booth, who still clutched my shoulder. I brought him down with me and for a moment we lay prostrate but rapidly recovering himself he sprang to his feet, dragging me up as I clung to his arm in terror. He shook himself free of my grasp and I sank down again, stunned and helpless. Then I became aware that Mr. Booth was kneeling at my side whispering encouraging words in my ear. He helped me to my feet and managed in spite of my total inability to speak to continue the scene to its close."

He had the obsession that certain articles were talismans of success if carried on his person during his performances. Moorish coins to jingle in his pocket when he played *Othello* and a crescent pin fastened to his scarf. An antique dagger for *Richard III,* a shabby old purse for *Sir Giles Overreach,* and the breast ornament worn by the rabbi in the synagogue beneath his *Shylock* gabardine.

Often he would carry these articles in his street clothes for the entire day of his appearance in these characters.

The anecdotes of Booth's mad adventures are innumerable, some of them are the results of drinking bouts, but more often they betray the aberrations of sheer insanity. Once on a voyage to fulfill an engagement in the South he was seized with a brooding melancholy and talked frequently to his companion, Thomas Flynn, of William Conway, a player who had committed suicide by jumping into the sea. As the vessel neared the spot where the unfortunate actor had perished Booth came hurriedly on deck saying he had a message for Conway and leaped into the ocean. A boat was lowered and after vast difficulty he was rescued. While being hauled into the boat he called to Flynn, "Look out, Tom—be steady. You're a heavy man: if the boat upsets we'll all be drowned."

It was this same Tom Flynn, one of his closest friends, who, after an evening's debauch in Charleston, found himself attacked. Booth had crawled through an open window in Flynn's room and was raining blows on his head with an iron fire-dog. In the mêlée that ensued Flynn succeeded in getting the better of the madman by a return blow which broke Booth's nose, disfiguring him for the remainder of his life.

Both in and out of the theatre his American career was marked by erratic conduct. His wild adventures were frequently succeeded by fits of remorse and brooding that would send him into hiding or to weeks at his Maryland home busied among his animals, his farming tools and his books. These lapses would then be succeeded by long periods of intensive industry in management and acting.

Engaged by Flynn for a short season in Annapolis, the company assembled in that town and waited day after day for Booth's appearance. His advertised performances were repeatedly cancelled. News came from the tragedian's wife that her husband had left Baltimore for Annapolis several days previously. Flynn was in despair when, a full week after the announced opening date, he was passing down the street and was accosted by a tattered urchin who asked if he was the manager.

"Why do you ask?" said Flynn.

"Because," replied the boy, "we've got one of your playing chaps aboard our sloop raising hell with the captain. You'd better come and take him away."

Following the lad, he reached a dirty little wood sloop in which Booth, for reasons known only to himself, had made the journey. He found his friend holding a musket leveled at the captain who was on his knees before him with a large bowl in his hands. Booth was exclaiming in tragic tones: "Drink, sir, drink. You're bilious and require physic. I know it by your eyes—by your skin. Drink or I'll send you to another and a better world." The captain howled with fear, declaring he had already drunk six bowls and this one would physic him to death.

Booth had discovered the medicine chest and was dosing the captain with salts.

One Sunday morning shortly after this Annapolis engagement certain orderly and pious citizens of Philadelphia were wending their way to church when they were dumfounded by the sight of a strange figure, costumed as *Hamlet* and mounted on a spirited circus horse, who addressed them thus:

> "Ladies and gentlemen, I intend to perform *Hamlet* to-night for the benefit of the poor, and a good play is worth forty sermons both for morals and reformation."

Then with a shout of "Join in chorus, citizens!" he sang:

> "O, 'tis my delight
> "Of a shiny night
> "In the season of the year."

Booth's sensitiveness to criticism, particularly from his audience, was extreme. During a Boston performance of EVADNE he exhibited a considerable uncertainty in the lines of *Ludovico*. Hisses and the sounds of disapproval rose over the footlights, at which Mr. Booth abruptly stopped in his performance and stepping forward said: "Ladies and gentlemen, I understand you well. Wilson's the boy for you. You'd better get him to finish the part. I've other business to attend to, so I wish you all good night." The Wilson referred to was a rival tragedian—and a very bad one—attached to the opposition house.

Having left EVADNE high and dry on the rocks he tore himself from restraining hands, saying, "I can't read. Take me to a lunatic asylum," doffed his costume and in great distress of mind walked the entire distance from Boston to Providence.

Another occasion when he snarled back at his audience for fancied disapprobation was in the tragedy of OROONOKO at Philadelphia. After *killing himself* in the last act he scrambled to his feet; stalking to the footlights he cried: "I'll serve you as General Jackson did—I'll *veto* you," evidently having in mind President Jackson's frequent and distressing veto messages.

Evidences of his antic disposition were constantly appearing. At one time in an attack of repugnance at the heartbreaks of an actor's life he proposed seriously to abandon it and applied for the position of lighthouse keeper at Cape Hatteras.

It is difficult to tell whether all of his escapades were the result of a deranged mind. Some of them have the appearance of the elaborate practical joking of a schoolboy: that for instance of the experience of the Reverend James Freeman Clarke—then a young clergyman in a western town, as related in THE ATLANTIC MONTHLY of September, 1861. He received a note from the tragedian which read:

"Sir—I hope you will excuse the liberty of a stranger addressing you on a subject he feels great interest in. It is to require a place of interment for his friend (s) in the churchyard, and also the expense attendant on the purchase of such place of temporary repose. Your communication on this matter will greatly oblige, Sir, your respectful and obedient servant, J. B. BOOTH."

The clergyman responded to this request by a visit to the actor's hotel. He describes him as a "short man, but one of those who seem tall when they choose to do so. He had a clear blue eye and fair complexion. In repose there was nothing to attract attention to him, but when excited his expression was so animated, his eyes so brilliant and his figure so full of life that he became another man."

After offering wine and cigars to his guest, Booth entertained him by reading aloud the whole of Coleridge's ANCIENT MARINER. He quite swept his hearer away by the magnetic fire of his recital.

"He actually," Mr. Clarke says, "thought himself the mariner—so I am persuaded—while he was reading."

The actor then entered upon an elaborate discussion with his visitor on Coleridge, Shelley and Keats, proceeded to argue his conceptions of Bible texts from a Bible which Booth ordered to be brought by the hotel waiter and concluded his entertainment by a recitation of Byron's "Lines to a Newfoundland Dog." After this he rose and taking a candle asked: "Would you like to look at the remains?"

The clergyman asked if the death of his friend was sudden.

"Very."

"Was he a relative?"

"Distant."

Says the narrator, "He led me into an adjoining chamber. I looked toward the bed in the corner of the room expecting to see a corpse. There was none there. But Booth went to another corner where, spread out upon a large sheet, I saw—*about a bushel of wild pigeons!*"

The clergyman declined to perform the obsequies, but he relates that Booth actually purchased a lot in the cemetery, had a coffin made, and went through a regular funeral service at the grave. "For several days he continued to visit the grave of his little friends and mourned over them with a grief which did not seem at all theatrical." This prank undoubtedly had serious underlying motive. Booth had a great sympathy for animals, birds and wild life, and the great slaughter of pigeons at that particular season had aroused his resentment. For three years he had been living on a purely vegetable diet, deeming it a sin to destroy anything that had life.

That Booth was but "mad north-northwest" was evident from his long periods of industry and conscientious behavior—periods when his acting aroused the deepest admiration from critics and excited his public to wild enthusiasm. But without warning the equilibrium of his brain would totter and he would become lost to his surroundings. His supporting actors were always a little afraid of him, and not without cause, for he had been known to refuse to die, as *Richard,* on Bosworth Field and to attack his *Richmond* so savagely as to back him off the scene, out through the stage door of the Bowery Theatre and to chase him, sword in hand, up the alley to the street and along the Bowery for several blocks. The passers-by were given the amazing spectacle of two armor-clad individuals, sword in hand, wigs and plumes astream, racing and clanking under the intermittent street-lamps.

One night at the Boston Theatre he had been announced for a performance of KING LEAR. The house was crammed with eager and impatient people. The hour for the curtain had gone by, but Booth had not arrived. Messengers were sent in every direction in an attempt to locate him, and were on the point of abandoning the search when he was discovered in one of his haunts surrounded by a ring of more or less inebriated listeners to whom he was pouring out verses of poetry, snatches of Shakespeare and quotations from the Bible. He protested he would not leave and fought the men who were trying to drag him to the theatre. He presently grew peacable and caught a glimmer of his responsibility.

While crossing the stage on his way to his dressing-room he became aware of the din on the other side of the curtain; the audience had grown frantic at the long delay and were becoming riotous. Booth demanded to know the reason for the clamor. He refused to listen to the importunings of his friends who were leading him to his dressing-room that he get ready for his part; he broke from them savagely, and running to the curtain pulled it aside.

Thrusting out his shoulders, he shook his fist at the howling mob.

"Shut up! Shut up!" he yelled.

The apparition of the drink-dyed face, the glaring eyes and the threatening gesture checked the racket for a moment.

"Keep quiet!" he cried, "you just keep still and in ten minutes I'll give you the God damnedest *King Lear* you ever saw in your life."

And he did: his first scene had hardly more than begun before he held the lately infuriated spectators in the hollow of his hand.

But this strangely perturbed spirit was not always in a turmoil. There were times of sweet serenity at his farm where he found solace among his books and interest in the rearing of his farm animals. Tom Hamblin, the actor, on the occasion of a visit to Booth was inclined to commiserate with him upon his loneliness. "You must be solitary here," he said.

"I am never without company," Booth replied, "I converse and hold counsel with the great and good of all ages. Look—there are Shelley and Byron and Wordsworth; here are rare Ben Jonson, Beaumont and Fletcher, Shakespeare and Milton: with them time never wearies. These are my companions, and I am never *less* alone than when alone."

It was in one of these retirements that he devoted himself to writing a play, UGOLINO, THE BANDIT, a turgidly romantic melodrama full of sound and fury which had some popularity when played by favorite tragedians, but I can not find that Booth ever appeared in it.

To the wife who survived him he was a tender husband and to the ten children she bore him a devoted father. His household was governed by rule. His daughter, Asia, writing of her father says: "His idea of home comprised a sacred circle wherein few were admitted save the immediate family." There was that in his nature which was deeply devotional. To all religions he gave the utmost respect—the Protestant, the Catholic and the Jewish. He knew the Koran and the Talmud as well as the Bible. He worshiped at many shrines, and never failed, in passing churches, to bare his head in reverence. Although much of his education had been of a desultory character he was of studious habits and had accumulated a knowledge both wide and useful. He had mastered French, speaking it with ease and proficiency. While acting in New Orleans he was engaged to give a performance of *Orestes* in Racine's ANDROMAQUE at the Théâtre

D'Orléans and succeeded so well that he was wholly in key with French actors who supported him.

Before all else Junius Brutus Booth was an actor and an enormously gifted one. He dramatized his emotions and placed them behind the footlights. To him Jaques' speech:

> "All the world's a stage,
> And all the men and women merely players,"

contained the philosophy of life. Thousands have attested to his power in the Shakespearean characters. As *Lear* and *Richard* he rose to remarkable heights while in *Pescara* and *Sir Giles Overreach* his acting was memorable.

On November 30, 1852, the turbulent life of the elder Booth came to an end. The fierce fires had burned out the vitality of his iron constitution. He died quite alone save for one sympathetic fellow passenger on a Mississippi steamboat at the age of fifty-six.

His last words were, "Pray, pray! pray!"

I once asked his son, Edwin, if he could tell me how his own acting differed from that of his father. "I think that mine is a little quieter," he said.

This letter of Junius Brutus Booth was found in the collection of Samuel H. Cowell, Theatre Royal, Edinburgh, addressed to

Joseph Cowell, Esqe.
Clark's Store,
Whitewater Township,
Hamilton County,
Ohio.

It was postmarked Louisville, Ky. Feb. 3, and franked, not stamped. It is a folded sheet, not an envelope.

"Year of the Christ
Feb. 3. 1834 "Exterior of Louisville Jail
of the Planet
5994 "Praise be to Allah!

"Your loving communication has been just delivered after my third incarceration in the above for carrying on solely an unprofitable and disgraceful business: namely—telling the Truth to Scoundrels. I have suffered much what is called physical pain—shammed more and feel (I wish I did not) more supreme contempt than ever of my own race. I wish I could *pity*—I can not. I can not say 'Forgive them, they know not what they do!'

"Per advice I hear you intend making money by sale of Hog's blood—in which is the life. It is none of my business—only be sure blood calls for blood: your horticultural notion I prefer, only be gentle in thy operations even then for there is a never dying worm. The Hindoo religion is the only one I believe to be at all like Truth—I feel so certain of it that were this my last moment & Death hanging over me on the very eve to stifle what tiny spark was lingering in my heart I would declare myself *Hindoo* versus quasidum.—Had there been no fish there would have been no Crucifixion—do you take? Excuse bad pen, hurry—dirty hands torn papers and Steamboat about to go. Many thanks to '*Moses*' & my best greetings to his caro maestro.

"Yrs ever

"J. B. Booth."

X

WILL-OF-AVON'S-NIGHT

April 23rd, 1916

X

WILL-OF-AVON'S-NIGHT

April 23rd, 1916

THE club had been deserted nearly all day, not a soul had entered the library. The sightless eyes of William Shakespeare glared from the copy of the Stratford bust over across at the rows of portraits of dead and gone actors in costume, and a few early spring flies buzzed about the thousand books on the theatre that filled the shelves. The printed lines on the pages of Fitzgerald Molloy's LIFE OF EDMUND KEAN, which I had been reading in the upholstered depths of my armchair, turned into small wriggly eels, and the light in the library grew soft and dim. Comfort stole over me like an anesthetic.

I could have sworn that I was alone, therefore I was at a loss to account for the quiet whisperings, the occasional grunt, and two or three distinct yawns.

It was then that Shakespeare's lower lip gave a sidewise protrusion as he blew upward at a fly crawling on his nose. Some one behind me sneezed, who it was I didn't look to see because I had become fascinated by Shakespeare's face. It had shed its plaster pallor. It was emphatically the face of a country gentleman—none but an out-of-door man could have shown that meaty hue of health—and what generous vintage had dyed purple the fine surface veins of the skin!

Shakespeare's left eyelid slid down. He winked not hurriedly, or wickedly, but a slow, deliberate, luscious wink, and a voice above my chair-back replied to the challenge with, "Good old Will!" It was a mellow voice, quiet, full-toned but with a trace of huskiness.

I knew it at once; it was the voice of David Garrick. There was a gleam of teeth beneath Shakespeare's tightly brushed mustache, now turned a good Saxon red, and I discovered evidence of faulty Elizabethan dentistry. "Why, lad, do you wear that unsightly ruff for *Richard?*" he asked, "*Richard* never wore a ruff."

"Our Drury Lane audience would boo me if I appeared without it," answered Davy. "Besides, Will, we've learned a thing about costume since your day. If it comes to that, didn't you wear a ruff when you were presented at Court? *Richard* was at Court, wasn't he?"

"Yes, lad, he *was* the Court."

"Oh, God! Garrick is at it again," exclaimed one down at the other end of the room. The tone was raucous, but somehow startlingly melodic. I turned in time to catch a dart from Edmund Kean's black eye. He came forward with a nervous stride, and stood before Garrick, his hands clasped and twitching behind his back, a devilish smile on his thin lips.

"Yes, he's always at it," said Shakespeare with a smile, slipping an affectionate hand under Kean's arm. "Mark his modern improvements to my ROMEO AND JULIET! Did you think, Davy, that I didn't know how my lovers should die when you contrived that abominable ending? Though you can fret me, you can not play upon me!"

"Leave off, William!" good-naturedly commanded another. "Good God! if you listened to those farthing tent-strollers you'd find that we knew nothing either of play-making or acting. I know 'em! Brainless tinkers."

It was Burbage, fat and scant of breath, who waddled over from under the fireplace. Garrick looked his contempt and muttered something, *sotto voce,* about "Old Scool!"

"Name of all the dullards!" cried George Frederick Cooke, who lay sprawled over a couch, not quite sober. "Can you find nothing more profitable to wrangle about? Come! a noggin! I'm dry as a salt herring."

Buzzing and murmurs rose crescendo like waking wind. Greetings and jests flew quite unchecked. Hands were clasped and thwacks descended on broad backs. Some one was singing the stave of a drinking song:

"Save your coppers; guard well your hose,
For a lusty wench whom every one knows
Is waiting her bit, but beware, friend mine,
No one can be trusted; take a cup of good wine!"

Then another with Sir Harry Bumper's song:

"Here's to the maiden of bashful fifteen,
And here's to the widow of fifty;
Here's to the flaunting, extravagant quean;
And here's to the huswif that's thrifty!
Let the toast pass; drink to the lass,
I'll warrant she'll prove an excuse for the glass."

I don't know where they got their pipes but long-stemmed churchwardens appeared like magic, and as the throng circled about Shakespeare, smoke went up from sacrificial fires. Love beamed from every eye and flowed toward the genial little man clad in good fustian doublet of mahogany hue—William of Avon! How he welcomed their greetings! Surely never was human smile sweeter than his, and what a motley, incongruous crowd it was that filled the library room, whose walls expanded until it became a vast hall! Chronological verity in speech and costume went glimmering. I thought the English stage might well be proud of its record as I beheld seventeenth-century Thomas Betterton deep in argument with Henry Irving—two noble figures on the theater's historic page. Irish Spranger Barry jostled Garrick's arm as he lurched against him, glass in hand, with——

"Ho, Davy, me boy! ye can't get the center of the stage to-night, for soft what light through yonder doorway breaks? It is the East, and Shakespeare is the sun! He knows your tricks, and what a damned bad *Romeo* you are."

Taking Sheridan's arm, Garrick stalked haught-

Courtesy of the Harvard College Library, Theatre Collection

William Shakespeare

ily away followed by Barry's jeers, in which Elliston joined with huge gusto.

Then came the rout: Doggett, Wilks, Mohun, Quin, Foote, Tate Wilkinson, Farren, Junius Brutus Booth, Fechter, Burton, John McCullough, quaint Nat Field in Elizabethan garb, doing a Morris dance with Dick Tarleton, Mossup, Macklin (a vast man, ages old), Samuel Phelps, Charles Matthews, Cibber, Cooper, Hamlin.

"What! Will the line stretch out till the crack of doom? Confound the fellows! Why don't they get in their historic order? Have they no sense of the march of time?"

"And what is time?" asked a quiet voice in my ear.

"Don't you know that Shakespeare was for *all* time?"

I looked into the eyes of Edwin Booth—eyes filled with gentle melancholy and twinkling with subtle humor. A fire of affection flashed through them as they lifted from mine and I followed their glance to where it rested on the Immortal Bard, now surrounded by a jubilant throng, shouting, singing and pledging his health.

Now, at a word Kean, Forrest and Gustavus Brooke made a dash to a group standing apart against the library shelves—academic-appearing men, whose sad looks were directed in emphatic disapproval toward the roystering actors. They picked out two pleasant-faced gentlemen whom I had not noticed and dragged them over in great glee to Shakespeare.

"Here they are, Will Hazlitt and Charley Lamb. They belong to us," shouted Kean. "If we leave them longer with that dry-as-dust crowd, they'll mummify."

To be sure; why hadn't I identified that sour little group before: Knight, Halliwell-Phillips, Schlegel, Warburton, the veritable dry-as-dust himself, and half a score of spectacled mourners. In the tumult I heard Will say:

"Fore God, lads! what do ye yonder? Those gentry crave wary walking. They've dismembered me—torn me limb from limb, so I find myself in sore straits to put myself together again. They've put into the words of my characters meanings that neither I nor they ever dreamed of. They've ground my poetry to dust, mixed it with water and turned it into mud pies. Odd's my life! I don't know my own *Hamlet!* And, who is this lunatic German fellow, Freud, who says that *Hamlet* was in love with his mother and jealous of his own father? Often I have told them that I am plain W. Shakespeare, gentleman, actor, playhouse manager, and maker of plays. They will naught of it, but keep on dissecting me."

Meanwhile, resentment marked the deportment of the dry-as-dust coterie at the assault that had carried off Hazlitt and Lamb. What I caught was:

Knight: Instead of our company, Shakespeare prefers the mummers!

Halliwell-Phillips: Singular taste!

Warburton: Outrageous! Why, they don't speak his language. How can they know his subtle philosophy—his cryptic meanings?

A symphony of sniffs was chorused by the whole group. Plainly the academic nose was out of joint.

A handful of players were staring at a poster fastened to the wall which they were discussing with some derision. Looking over their shoulders I read this:

"THE QUEEN TO SECRETARY WALSINGHAM

"January 25, 1586.

"The daily abuse of stage playes is such an offence to the godlye and so grete a hindrance to the gospel, as the Papists doe exceedingly rejoice at the blemish thereof, and not without cause. For every daye in the week the Players' bills are set uppe in sundry places of the city, some in the name of Her Majesty's men, some th' Erle of Leicester's, some th' Erle of Oxford's, the Lord Admiral's, and divers others—so that when the bells toll to the Lecturers the trumpettes sound to the Stagers. The Play-houses are pestered when the Churches are naked. At the one it is not possible to get a place, at the other void seats are plenty.

"It is a woful sight to see two hundred proude players jet in their silkes, where five hundred poore people starve in the stretes. But if this mischife must be tolerated, let every stage in London pay a weekly pension to the poore, that *ex hoc malo proveniat aliquod bonum.* But it were rather to be wished that players might be used as Apollo did laughing, *semel in anno.*"

To this document was attached the name of royal ELIZABETH.

"What, Elizabeth! The Queen wrote that?"

"The red-headed termagant!"

"Aye," replied the portly Burbage, "but 'twas when she was overcome with megrims through a quarrel with the Earl of Leicester. Didn't she have the players to her palace to perform TWELFTH NIGHT and THE MERRY WIVES? And I have with my own eyes seen a letter she wrote to Will that commenced 'Dear William.' The Queen knew well enough how to laugh. And oaths were as common as prayers to her dainty lips."

But, who is here? A woman? Who let her in? Club rules clearly say that ladies are not admitted. In costume too! The hussy! This is really too bad! What! A churchwarden pipe between her lips? They're turning the place into a brothel!

The creature was shameless in her freedom of the place, and the men did not seem to regard her presence as an occasion for the slightest show of gallantry. I marveled at this for the moment was riotous and the wench was truly comely. What an eye she had, and what a perfect oval was her face! My mystification ended in a shock, when Dickey Suett remarked:

"Very pretty frock for *Ophelia*, Kynaston, but you'd look vastly better if you'd shave."

Kynaston, the boy actress of the King's comedians at Blackfriars, the love-lorn *Juliet*, the gentle *Ophelia*, the sprightly *Rosalind;* the Julian Eltinge of his day!

Now began the songs again, and staves of THE LEATHER BOTTEL were chanted lustily. At the end of the room where hundreds of candles made a wondrous blaze of light, a platform had been erected, carpeted in green and strewn with tender leaves. Two big oaken chairs stood in the middle, carelessly hung with early spring flowers. Below this was a long refectory table laden with joints of beef, boars' heads, pasties, trenchers of bread and meat puddings. Towering above the generous fare was a punch bowl filled to the brim, presided over by an actor whom I failed to identify in the costume of *Falstaff*—a veritable mountain of flesh. Toward the banquet the crew took its way in not altogether steady procession, Shakespeare raised on the shoulders of four stalwart fellows. They seated the poet gently in one of the chairs of the dais, and Kynaston, now costumed as *Cleopatra,* crowned him with laurel.

Cups were filled, THE LEATHER BOTTEL roared out in rich harmony. Shakespeare's health was pledged in a shout like a cannonade.

Two sober-visaged men stood on the outer edge of the throng, looking with something like toleration upon the scene. One was of majestic height with classic features and immobile lips; the other, lesser in figure, and with marks of petulance and temper in his expressive face. No one could mistake them—John Philip Kemble and Macready! They had the air of men performing their duty awkwardly, but determinedly, and not knowing quite how to do it. But they pledged with fervor, they even sang, but sang as men to whom music is a strange noise.

Shakespeare's face shone like the sun.

Kean, Liston and the Elder Booth came butting forward in the crowd with a brace of captives, and truly a sorry pair. Never looked I on unhappier countenances. These were the two arch-flagellants and inquisitors of the Theatre—their Reverences, William Prynne and Jeremy Collier. Oh, Masters, the mummers have you on the hip now! Expect no mercy! In an instant they were garlanded with flowers and crowned with gilt coronets. A claymore was thrust into Prynne's left hand, a scepter into Collier's; and they stood seething in wrath, a goblet of punch in their right hand.

Kean, who has the spirit of the fiend in him to-night, touches his finger-tips in churchly sanctity and, rolling his hypocritical eyes upward, wails, "Verily brethren, we walk in the paths of iniquity, and consort with children of the pit, the spawn of the theatre! Get thee behind me, Satan!"

The lament is greeted with a howl of derision.

"Bumpers, you Puritans!"

"To the Theatre!"

"You roasted us once; you'll toast us now!"

The cups are forced to livid lips; Collier makes a sickly show of appearing to treat the matter as a joke, but Prynne is stern, silent, immovable; his lips tightly pressed, his body rigid with a martyr's determination.

There was an instant's silence and the unhappy pair were swept away and forgotten.

The gaiety was at its climax.

I looked back from my perch of vantage on the library table into the dim recesses of the room and discovered it was not deserted as I had expected to find it. A protesting knot of men were holding an animated meeting which appeared quite unrelated to the revels yonder. A wan individual, who continually swept his dank black hair from his forehead, was demanding with excited gesticulation:

"How long must Francis Bacon wait for vindication? Gentleman, look at this date,"—pointing to the calendar set at April 23, 1916.—"Three hundred years ago to-day there was buried in the chancel of Trinity Church at Stratford-on-Avon one who fathered a fraud, and who has fostered it through the centuries, a dissipated, sordid-minded, theatrical manager; a noted plagiarist, pilferer of others' thoughts, appropriator of the most glorious poetry the world has ever known. Look there! Such complacency! Ugh! The thief!" and he fumed himself into speechlessness.

At which Ignatius Donnelly began, "If you will glance over this key-sheet you will see by the alphabetical succession that my cipher proves the Baconian authorship beyond question."

Now all commenced to speak at once: Edwin Reed, Doctor Owen, Lord Penzance, Doctor Theobold. The most insistent was a little round, red person, for all the world like the Phiz drawings of

Mr. Pickwick who, through his cryptogrammic invention, was enabled to trace in every alternate scene of the tragedies, and every tenth, seventeenth and thirty-second line of the comedies, the names of Francis Bacon, F. Bacon, Fr. Bacon, etc. etc., *ad nauseam.* Each one had his own angle of indisputable proof that the great poet-dramatist of the Elizabethan era was none other than Lord Bacon. On the near-by couch lounged a man, heavy eyebrowed, sheaved in white hair like a venerable lion. From his narrowed eyelids shot a glance full of shrewdness and humor. He was smoking an enormous cigar. When the wranglers had talked themselves breathless, he blew a heavy cloud of smoke into the air, and with a sharp look down to where the poet was being fêted, remarked in Mark Twain's unmistakable drawl, "Shakespeare? There ain't no such animile."

Meanwhile pandemonium was stirring among the revelers. John Philip had got his gait now; self-consciousness had vanished; with the majestic oratory of the Kembles he was reciting *Hamlet's* lines with obvious application to their author: "How noble in reason! How infinite in faculty! In form and moving how express and admirable! In action how like an angel! In apprehension how like a god! The beauty of the world! The paragon of animals!"

The contagion of his emotion spread, and, wonder of wonders! Forrest and Macready fell on each other's necks. I felt myself going decidedly mad!

Crash! Who put out the lights? A stream of

ghostly figures glided by me, and I heard the same whisperings and murmurs that I had heard—one? two? three hours ago? I can not tell.

I was in a deucedly cramped position in the arm-chair. Fitzgerald Molloy's LIFE OF KEAN had fallen to the floor. A grayish dawn was coming through the windows from Gramercy Park, and from some chicken coop over on Third Avenue I heard a cock crow.

I stared up at Shakespeare; he was smiling.

Thought I, that smile will live

"Till time is old and hath forgot itself,
And blind oblivion hath swallowed cities up,
And mighty states have gone to dusty nothing."

The superintendent has reported to the house committee that the workmen in cleaning the library busts had chipped a piece from the corner of Shakespeare's mouth. There is no trace of breakage that I can find, however, but there is a distinct change in the expression. Shakespeare smiled.

THE END

THE ART CLUB OF PHILADELPHIA

Snow Song

For Devin — A.K.R.

To my family, with love — D.L.

Kids Can Press gratefully acknowledges the financial support of the Government of Ontario, through Ontario Creates; the Ontario Arts Council; the Canada Council for the Arts; and the Government of Canada for our publishing activity.

Published in Canada and the U.S. by Kids Can Press Ltd.
25 Dockside Drive, Toronto, ON M5A 0B5

Kids Can Press is a Corus Entertainment Inc. company

www.kidscanpress.com

The artwork in this book was rendered in gouache, pencil crayon and Photoshop.
The text is set in Andes.

Edited by Yvette Ghione
Designed by Marie Bartholomew

Printed and bound in Buji, Shenzhen, China, in 5/2020 by WKT Company

CM 20 0 9 8 7 6 5 4 3 2 1

LIBRARY AND ARCHIVES CANADA CATALOGUING IN PUBLICATION

Title: Snow song / A.K. Riley ; Dawn Lo.

Names: Riley, A. K., author. | Lo, Dawn, 1992– illustrator.

Identifiers: Canadiana 20190214856 | ISBN 9781525302350 (hardcover)

Subjects: LCGFT: Picture books.

Classification: LCC PS8635.I535 S56 2020 | DDC jC813/.6 — dc23

Snow Song

A.K. Riley • Dawn Lo

Kids Can Press

Fine pearls of snow

Then a twirl of snow.

Around the eaves

A curl of snow.

Through black thread trees

Swirls the snow.

The winter wind

Unfurls the snow —

A long, white

Glittering

Lash of snow.

Faster

Faster

Faster

Snow.

The sky's unraveling

Into snow—

The pond is lathering up

With snow —

The hills are knitted caps

Of snow.

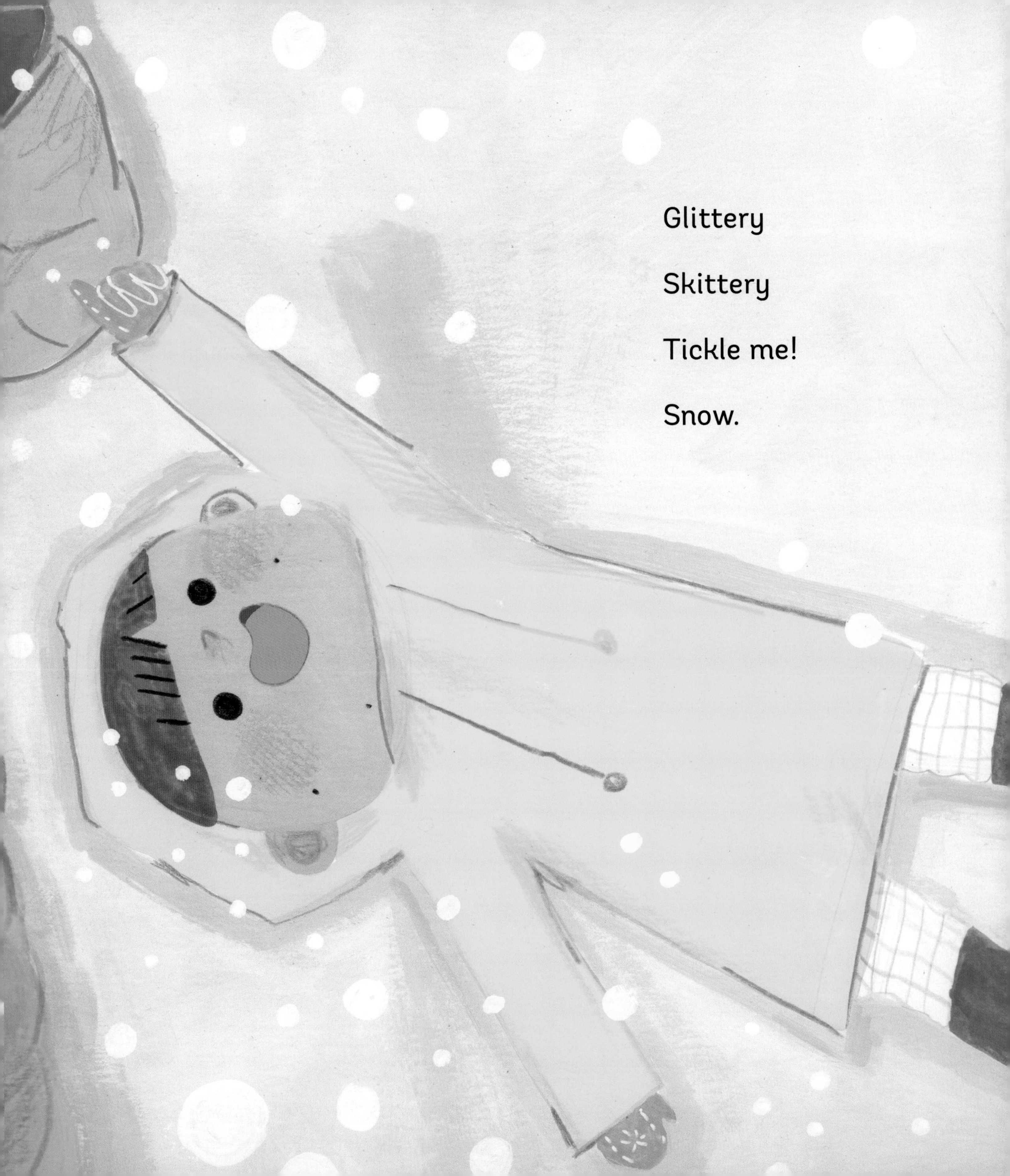

Glittery

Skittery

Tickle me!

Snow.

Slow ...

The world is swaddled

Snug in snow.

Time to dawdle,

Says the snow.

We waddle through

The creamy snow ...

Dreaming

Dreaming

Dreaming

Snow.

So soft the snow,

Froths the snow

Upon the trees

And spangled streams —

Up to my knees!

Shimmer and flow —

I love the snow.

I love the snow!

Above the snow

One pearl of snow:

The moon, aglow.

Unworldly

Kindly shining snow!

And all the stars

All the stars

Bright falling stars

Are made of

Snow.